Anatomy
of the
Ship

The Type VII U-Boat

**Anatomy
of the
Ship**

The Type VII
U-Boat

David Westwood

CONWAY

MARITIME PRESS

Frontispiece. *U 99* on the day of her launch, 19
September 1940. Originally *U 69*, her number was
changed in an attempt to convince Germany's
enemies and the neutral countries that the
submarine fleet was much larger than they
thought. Here, the whole of the external section
of the pressure hull can be seen, as well as the
deck casing, and the fore and aft hydroplanes.

Reprinted 1986

First published in Great Britain 1984 by
Conway Maritime Press Ltd
24 Bride Lane, Fleet Street
London EC4Y 8DR

ISBN 0 85177 314 1

Designed by Geoff Hunt
Typeset by Witwell Ltd, Liverpool
Printed and bound in Great Britain by
Cambridge University Press

Contents

FOREWORD

In a number of ways this volume departs from the pattern established for the 'Anatomy of the Ship' series by the first two volumes. The most obvious difference is the coverage, which relates not to a single ship but a whole class – and a class which was built in large numbers and in many variations. Furthermore, the submarine is a relatively small warship and has few of the external features which take up such a large part of earlier titles in this series. With these factors in mind, therefore, it was decided that *The Type VII U-boat* would concentrate on depicting the development of the design through its numerous stages. Ship modellers, who make up a significant proportion of the readership of the series, are unlikely to be so concerned with internal fittings as those visible externally, so the detail drawings are mainly confined to the latter.

ACKNOWLEDGEMENTS

The author has many people to thank: Michael Simpson and Alan Lloyd of University College, Swansea; R M Coppock and the Naval Historical Branch, Ministry of Defence; Antony Preston; Ian V Hogg; Eberhard Rössler; Herr Korff and Herr Alexander of Blohm und Voss; the Librarian and Staff of Grantham Public Library; Norman Friedman; and over 50,000 German submariners of the Second World War, many of whom failed to return from operations.

BIBLIOGRAPHY

Unpublished material
Blohm und Voss Drawings of *U 995* (for refit 1970–1971)
Friedrich Krupp (Germaniawerft) Drawings No A 01055, A 01056, A 01057, A 01058
Royal Norwegian Navy Drawings (3) of *Kaura* ex-*U 995*

Published material
Büchheim, L-G, *U-Boat War*, New York 1978
Gröner, E, *Die deutschen Kriegsschiffe 1815–1945*, Munich 1968
Jane's Fighting Ships, Volumes for 1935 to 1948
Lohmann/Hildebrand, *Kriegsmarine 1939–1945*, Munich 1956–1964
Rohwer/Hümmelchen, *Chronology of the War at Sea 1939–1945*, 2 vols, London 1972 and 1974
Rössler, E, *Die deutschen Uboote und Ihre Werften*, 2 vols, Munich 1979
——— *Die Torpedos der deutschen U-boote*, Herford, 1984
——— *Geschichte des deutschen Ubootbaus*, Munich 1975

Introduction

At 21 minutes to eight in the evening of 3 September 1939, the SS *Athenia*, outward bound from Liverpool to Montreal with 1400 passengers, was struck by a torpedo. This was the first attack in the Second World War to be made by the German Navy, and the torpedo was fired by *U30*, a Type VII U-boat, commissioned in 1936. On 10 July 1945, the British steam fishing boat *Kned* was sunk by mine off Lizard Head, in a minefield laid in August 1944 by *U 218*, a VIID U-boat, commissioned in 1942. Thus the German naval war began and ended in submarine action.

Despite the operations carried out by the more glamorous surface ships, such as *Bismarck*, *Graf Spee*, *Scharnhorst* and *Tirpitz*, the major effort of this war was made by the Submarine Arm, which began hostilities with 57 boats, of which just 18 were Type VIIs. At that time (September 1939) neither side had an inkling of what effect these boats would have as hostilities continued for five years and nine months, although Britain had instituted convoy sailing as early as August that year. Admiral Raeder, Commander-in-Chief of the German Navy, and Admiral Dönitz, Commander of the Submarine Arm, were agreed at the time that the German Navy could contribute little to the war apart from showing that its men knew 'how to die gallantly'.

The early stages of the war resulted in some singular successes for the U-boats: Prien and *U 47* entered Scapa Flow and (after a number of attempts) sank the *Royal Oak* at her moorings; Schuhart in *U 29* sank HMS *Courageous* at sea; von Tiesenhausen (*U 331*) sank HMS *Barham*. But throughout this period, and the much longer one that followed it, the main task of the U-boats was not in single handed derring-do, but the ceaseless grind of sinking merchant vessels, and most particularly merchant vessels in the North Atlantic that were supplying food, stores, weapons and ammunition from the vast manufacturing and supply warehouses of the Americas. If the U-boats could deny Britain the supplies that sailed across the Atlantic, Germany could count on the United Kingdom not only being removed from active participation in the war, but the island itself would be denied to America as a stepping-stone to Europe for the necessary invasion. The stakes were extremely high, and the German Navy soon invested all that it could afford in submarines, for the surface fleet never achieved the strength and balance planned by Raeder.

Once the French Atlantic ports had been captured, the U-boats increased their range and their rate of operation, for they no longer had to circumnavigate the British Isles (the Channel was denied them by the Dover mine barrage); from the West Coast of France the Type VII boats could now reach out into the western part of the North and Central Atlantic, as well as operating in the Mediterranean and in the vicinity of the Azores and Gibraltar. For many months Dönitz suffered from a continual shortage of boats; this was due to Hitler's almost total lack of understanding of sea power, especially the importance of the North Atlantic, both strategically and economically. When Russia was invaded, the supply of steel and manpower became even shorter, and Dönitz waged a running battle with the Army for enough of both to build and crew the boats he needed to increase U-boat strength. He also campaigned – but in this instance lost – for a naval air arm. All he obtained were a few Focke-Wulf Fw 200 'Kondor' aircraft for aerial reconnaissance (many of which were almost continually grounded). Consequently he had no eyes constantly over the Atlantic watching for his targets – the convoys.

However he did evolve one tactic which optimised the performance of the Type VII. Underwater it had a low speed, but on the surface they could make 16-17 knots; Dönitz reasoned that if the U-boats were to have any chance of attacking the convoys successfully, they would have to go in on the surface, and at night. In daytime they could range the shipping lanes freely, looking for their targets, and report positions and courses to his headquarters so that he could order concentrations of boats for devastating attacks at night. This tactic proved extremely successful, the more so when the most experienced commanders – such as Prien, Kretschmer, Schepke, Schultze and others – actually began to go inside the convoys at night, firing their torpedoes from a mere two or three hundred metres. They reaped a terrible harvest.

By 1941 there was a distinct increase in the overall strength of the U-boat arm, and this was maintained, despite increasing losses, almost to the end of the war. The overall effectiveness of the arm began to fall however, from mid-1943. Allied countermeasures, initially woefully lacking, improved to such an extent that they eventually denied to the U-boats their one advantage – the ability to operate on the surface at night. By May 1943 the era of the Type VII was almost over: in the three months from March the Allies' combination of centimetric radar, seaborne direction-finding equipment, and very long range patrol and attack aircraft, coupled with increasing strengths and co-ordination of convoy escorts and successful anti-submarine tactics, forced Dönitz to withdraw the U-boats from the North Atlantic convoy routes, to seek safer targets elsewhere.

They enjoyed little peace in the more remote areas however, for a tactic that had proved unsuccessful initially – task forces hunting U-boats, rather than defending convoys – now reappeared with the advent of the escort carrier hunter group. Spearheaded by the US Navy, the hunter-killer groups soon had significant successes. This sudden reversal at sea forced the German Navy onto the defensive until such time as the new Type XXI boats (with a high underwater speed) were ready to go to sea. Happily for the Allies, the northern European land campaign was going so well that those boats never saw service in numbers. Had they done so, the war might have dragged on for a considerably longer time.

The Type VII was designed, above all, as a submersible torpedo-boat. It had none of the advantages of its nuclear descendants: able to stay underwater at speed for perhaps a few hours, and only any longer if unmoving, they were *forced* to the surface because they had insufficient (battery) power for long submerged operations. Thus battery-charging by running the diesel engines was mandatory. This was of no great import in the earlier part of the war, because air patrols were intermittent and very inexperienced. By May 1943 surfacing was fraught with danger, and standing orders from Admiral Godt (who took command of the Submarine Arm when Dönitz became C-in-C of the Navy) instructed captains to run on the surface with the boat in neutral buoyancy, with one diesel and one electric motor running, and to be ready to dive at all times.

The Schnorchel, adapted by the Germans from captured devices fitted to the Royal Dutch Navy 'O' type boats, now came into its own, together with a number of increasingly effective (but often too late, and always in short supply) electronic countermeasures. Indeed, it was in the period 1943 to 1945 that the foundations of present-day ECM were laid.

The Type VII may well have become out-dated, but it still found itself involved in all the theatres of naval warfare which it had the range to reach. In all, the Type VII was operating from Bear Island in the Arctic Ocean to the Bermudas and beyond, and from Greenland to Gibraltar, as well as into the Mediterranean. It was the largest class of submarines ever built (704 boats altogether), and certainly sank the lion's share of the total Allied and neutral shipping losses during the Second World War.

THE DEVELOPMENT OF THE TYPE VII

The history of German submarine involvement goes back to 1902, when a Spanish submarine designer, d'Equivelley, drew plans for the *Forelle*, an all-electric boat, which served as the forerunner for many hundreds of subsequent boats. The First World War showed what the submarine could do in economic warfare, and the decision in favour of the Allies was a fine one, dictated far more by events on land and in politics than at sea. One of the decisive factors on land was the injection of large numbers of fresh troops into France from America. Although not winning the battles, they boosted morale and stiffened the

otherwise depleted and almost exhausted defensive lines, and paved the way for decisive advances.

The war over, the submarine threat Germany had posed to Great Britain and France remained high in the consideration of the peace-makers: the Treaty of Versailles banned all manufacture of submarines in Germany, and eliminated her submarine fleet by confiscation. With her surface fleet almost emasculated, and her armaments firms forced back to making metaphorical plough-shares, the Germany Navy had recourse to one expedient only – subterfuge. In the 1920s covert companies were established to research armoured fighting vehicles, artillery, aircraft, surface ships and submarines, and many other aspects of the military art. None was more successful than the *Ingenieurskaantor vor Scheepsbouw* IvS), established in the Hague, which was entirely devoted to the study of the submarine. Design types of the late First World War period were scrutinised, and new designs and modifications put on paper.

The whole process would have been purely academic had not the strategic possibilities of the submarine, and its value as a coastal defender, been made abundantly clear by operations carried out during World War I. Nations with little need for battleships could see that the submarine could quite easily prove the cheaper countermeasure to the *Dreadnought* and its succeeding classes. Wilhelm Bauer, in the 1860s had designed two submarines, and he saw them rendering the enormous big-gun ships impotent. Seventy years later countries such as Finland, Turkey and Spain agreed with this view, although the Royal Navy was still suspicious of the submariner, seeing him not far removed from a pirate.

The countries mentioned, as well as Russia, Italy, Argentina, Estonia, Chile, Rumania, Japan, Yugoslavia, the Netherlands, China, Uruguay, Sweden, Portugal, Norway, Brazil and Bulgaria, all contacted IvS for design studies, and nine boats to these studies were actually built before Germany was allowed once more to possess a submarine arm in her navy. Boats were built for (and generally in) Turkey, Finland, Spain, Sweden, Russia and Rumania. Of these, the Spanish *E 1*, the Swedish *Delfin* and the Rumanian *Marsuinul* all contributed to what was to become the German Type VII class.

In 1935 the London Naval Agreement was signed; the actual outcome of the conference was decided on the first day, when the German delegation announced that Germany wanted 35 per cent of the Royal Navy tonnage, and 45 per cent in submarines. If they did not get agreement on these figures, they had, they said, instructions to go home. The British Government and the Admiralty agreed, and further acquiesced in the near demand that Germany could increase her submarine strength to 100 per cent of that of the Royal Navy, should it be deemed desirable by the Germans, and after consultation with the Admiralty in Britain. Needless to say, there was no consultation, but the German submarine strength was almost equal to that of the Royal Navy in September 1939.

To return to *E 1*, the plans were examined in detail by the German

Navy, and the design was put on a list of three types which were to be built, clandestinely if necessary, when the Armed Forces were able to re-equip. The arrival of Hitler as Chancellor, and soon Commander-in-Chief of the Armed Forces, meant immediate action in recruitment and rearmament for all three forces, although it was not until March 1935, that the Treaty of Versailles was unilaterally abrogated. Then came the London Naval Agreement, although the U-boats to form the 1st U-boat Flotilla, under the (then) Captain Dönitz, were already very close to being launched. Initially the Germans built the very simple, quick-to-complete, Type II boats; these were more for numbers than any thought of strategic value. The first Type VII boat (*U 27*) was laid down (order number 908 at A G Weser) on 11 November 1935, launched on 24 June 1936, and commissioned on 12 August 1936. This boat was the first of 704 boats of the class.

Building went on very slowly until the war was a year old. In the pre-war years Hitler kept assuring Raeder that war would not come until 1944, and so the C-in-C (Navy) planned to build a balanced fleet, with a number of aircraft carriers (possibly four in all), together with some of the most modern and powerful capital ships afloat; these were to be supported by adequate cruisers, destroyers and smaller craft, and a submarine arm of 221 U-boats by 1947. This would have been a formidable force, qualitatively an equal to any European fleet then in being.

War became inevitable far earlier that Hitler and his Grand Admiral believed. The Polish adventure turned into a European war, and the German Navy had very few submarines at all. Added to the paucity of numbers was the initial fear that America would enter the war at the slightest provocation. This led to restrictions being put on U-boat operations (and underscored heavily by the *Athenia* incident) so that the Type VII boats, and their larger sisters, the Type IXs, were unable at the outset to realise their full potential.

The basic *E 1* design was modified four times in 1928. The first design, of February, had six internal compartments, and was 47.95 metres long (pressure hull). The compartments were: bow torpedo compartment; accommodation compartment; control room; diesel engine compartment; electric motor compartment; stern torpedo compartment. In the next three designs this was extended to 7 compartments and 54.25 metres, by the addition of a second accommodation compartment, designed for the senior rates, aft of the control room. Ordinary seamen slept forward, among the torpedoes.

The boat was 755 tons surface displacement, 965 tons submerged. She was fitted with two 1400hp diesels and two 500 hp electric motors, giving her a maximum surface speed of 17 knots, and a maximum 8.5 knots underwater (this latter speed being of short duration). Carrying nearly 117 tons of fuel oil, she had a surface range of 11,200 nautical miles at 10 knots (her best cruising speed), and her batteries gave her a submerged range of 180 nautical miles at just 2.5 knots. This slow underwater speed was not considered problematic, because anti-submarine weapons and tactics were still in their infancy, and Asdic

was no more at that time than a fond wish of the steering committee.

So it was that the earlier UB type boats of the First World War were merely modified and uprated in power, and for this very reason their success was later to be severely limited. But the state of the art in 1930 was far removed from that of 1943. By 1933 a number of boat designs were being considered by the German Navy, some of which were adopted. The Type IA, of which only two were built, was a 500-ton design, which manifested appalling underwater performance characteristics; no more of this class were built. The Type II coastal boats have already been mentioned; it is sufficient to say that their range and torpedo capacity rendered them impractical for strategic warfare. The Type III was a hybrid, designed to carry two motor boats on the after casing in a watertight cylinder, but the design was not developed. The same fate befell Types IV (a supply and generating boat), and Types V and VI (both numbers being reserved for test boats with single propulsion units, capable of surface and submerged running). But the Type VII saw service in seven different forms, and two forms which did not come to fruition. Those that saw service were:

Type	VII	10 boats built
	VIIB	24 boats built
	VIIC and C/41	660 boats built
	VIID	6 boats built
	VIIF	4 boats built
		Totalling 704 boats built

(This figure of 704 is of a grand total of 1152 submarines built during the period 1935 – 1945, disregarding the very small classes and Walter boats.) There were seven further designs under consideration (VIII, IX, X, XI, XII, XIII, XIV) of which three (IX, X, XIV) were built; all were much larger boats, designed to operated individually. Thus no less than 61 per cent of all German submarines constructed under Hitler's regime were of the Type VII class.

The designer of the Type VII, Schürer, based his work on the UB III class of World War I, modified in the light of the experience gained in building by IvS for the foreign customers mentioned above. The form of the boat was that of a cylindrical pressure hull, with bow and stern welded on to the fore and aft sections of the pressure hull. The addition of external casing was to give the boats some sea-keeping capability, which was denied to the simple cylinder of the pressure hull. They were all single-hulled boats, and the drawings show that the pressure hull emerges amidships. A casing deck was added, and the attack centre (frequently called the conning-tower in other countries) also had a casing, in this case designed to improve weather protection on the surface, and enhance underwater performance by reducing water resistance.

Internally the boats always had the following compartments:
Forward torpedo compartment and crew's quarters
Officers' and chief rates' accommodation

Control room with attack centre above

Senior rates' accommodation

Diesel engine room

Electric motor room

After torpedo compartment (although this was occasionally contiguous with the electric motor room).

Power then was provided by the diesels and the electric motors, and steering on the surface by engine manipulation and the rudder(s) aft. Diving, attitude and surfacing was controlled by a combination of the buoyancy of the boat (positive, neutral or negative), forward speed, and the angle of the two sets of hydroplanes.

External weapons comprised, at first, a main deck gun (8.8cm) and a single anti-aircraft (FlaK) cannon, usually of 2cm calibre. This, as will be seen from the Drawings, was altered considerably after the events of the spring of 1943, until a few U-boats were equipped as aircraft traps, an experiment which soon proved of no significant value. But the main armament of the submarine is the torpedo, and the torpedoes used were mainly Types G7a and G7e, with the issue later in the war of *Zaunkönig*, *LUT* and *FAT* type weapons.

The boats were designed with as much of their length forward of the engine room to increase their sea-keeping qualities, and this led to a short stern, in turn cutting the diving time considerably. The original tests of performance indicated that once saddle-tanks were fitted (to increase the boats' capacity to carry fuel oil, and with complementary ballast and diving tanks) performance was worse at surface speeds of 11-13 knots, but improved between 14 and 18 knots. As the range of the boats was increased significantly by the addition of the saddle-tanks, they were retained. What was equally important was the fact that even with saddle-tanks, the boats could submerge in just 30 seconds, more than adequate until the end of the war.

It has already been mentioned that of the Type VII class, the large majority were of VIIC variant; in fact there were 572 VIIC boats built, and 88 VIIC/41 (the VIIC/41 was identical to the VIIC except that the steel used was a higher grade (Ww), and capable of withstanding greater water pressure: this meant an increased operating depth and great survivability in depth-charge attacks).

When Dönitz (now C-in-C, U-boats) looked at the boats available to him in 1936, he decided that the only boat that would continue to be built after initial orders (for Types IA, II, VII and IX) had been completed, would be the Type VII class. However, experiences with the Type VII (original form) required some modifications to be made, and these are shown in the details of the individual types below. (The Type IX also got a new lease of life as operations spread westward in the Atlantic.) In general terms, the class increased in displacement, range, torpedo-carrying capacity and offensive/defensive armament, as well as being increasingly more elaborately equipped with ECM sets of varying function and efficiency. But the basic form of the boats (even when drastically lengthened – see Types VIID and F, below, and in the Drawings Section), remained as in the original. The general opinion of the boats was favourable from the officers' and crews' point of view, and they proved their worth in the Battle of the Atlantic, for which they were mainly responsible.

Tables

TABLE 1: TYPE TYPE VII (ORIGINAL FORM)

Displacement:	Surface 626 tons, submerged 745 tons, (submerged, fully loaded and manned 915 tons)
Length overall:	Casing 64.51 metres, pressure hull 45.5 metres
Beam:	Casing 5.85 metres, pressure hull 4.7 metres
Keel to bridge overall:	9.5 metres
Draught (boat surfaced):	4.37 metres
Engines:	2 MAN 6-cylinder 4-stroke M6V 40/46 diesels totalling 2100-2310bhp
	Maximum revolutions 470-485rpm
	Maximum surface speed 16-17 knots
	Range 6200 sea miles at 10 knots; 2900 sea miles at 16 knots; Combined diesel/electric drive range 6800 sea miles at 10 knots
	Fuel oil 67 tons in all, of which 58.6 tons within the pressure hull
Motors:	2 BBC (Brown Boveri & Co) GG UB 720/8 electric motors totalling 750shp
	Maximum revolutions (geared down) 322 rpm
	Maximum submerged speed 8 knots
	Range underwater 73-94 sea miles at 4 knots
	Batteries Us 27, 31 - 33, 35, 36: 2 x 62-cell AFA type 27 MAK 740 producing 6940 amp hours. Us 28 - 30, 34: 2 x 62-cell AFA Type 33 MAL 740 producing 8480 amp hours
Builders:	Us 27 - 32 Deschimag, Bremen
	Us 33 - 36 Germaniawerft, Kiel
Built:	1935 - 1936
Designed:	The Type VII (sometimes, but erroneously, called the Type VIIA) was designed in 1933-34. Single-hulled submersible fitted with saddle-tanks (after they had been tested, as noted above). Six compartments, with internal trim tanks in Compartments I (aft torpedo room) and VI (forward torpedo room). Main diving tank and fuel oil tank under the control room. Regulating tanks (internal and external to pressure hull) pressure-tight, except for auxiliary tanks in the saddle-tanks. Additional diving tanks in bows and stern. Diving depth 100 metres, crush depth 200 metres. Diving times 50 seconds (normal); 30 seconds (neutral buoyancy)
Armament:	5-53.3cm (21in) torpedo tubes. Four in bow torpedo room and one external casing tube astern (non-reloadable). Bow tubes reloadable, and fitted below the constructed waterline. 11 torpedoes carried, or 22 TMA (torpedo calibre mines) or 33 TMB.
	1-8.8cm C35 L/45 gun fitted forward of the tower; 1-2cm C30 aft of tower
Crew:	4 officers and 40 ratings
Boats:	1 dinghy, stowed under the forward casing, forward of the torpedo loading hatch

TABLE 2: THE TYPE VIIB

Displacement:	Surface 704 tons (dry), 753 tons (fuel and water tanks full); submerged 857 tons, fully loaded and crewed 1040 tons
Length overall:	Casing 66.5 metres, pressure hull 48.8 metres
Beam:	Casing 6.2 metres, pressure hull 4.7 metres
Keel to bridge overall:	9.5 metres
Draught (boat surfaced):	4.74 metres
Engines:	As Type VII but with superchargers (Us 45-50 2 Germaniawerft 6-cylinder 4-stroke F46 diesels with superchargers) totalling 2800-3200bhp
	Maximum revolutions 470 - 490rpm
	Maximum surface speed 17.2 - 17.9 knots
	Ranges 8700 sea miles at 10 knots; 3850 sea miles at 17.2 knots; combined diesel/electric drive range 9400 (from U 51 onwards 9700) sea miles at 10 knots
	Fuel oil maximum 108.3 tons; normal load 99.7 tons, of which 57.3 tons within the pressure hull
Motors:	2 AEG GU 460/8-276 electric motors totalling 750shp
	Maximum revolutions (geared down) 295rpm
	Maximum submerged speed 8 knots
	Range underwater 90 sea miles at 4 knots (reduced compared with Type VII due to greater displacement of VIIB)
	Batteries Us 45, 47, 51: 2 x 62-cell AFA 27 MAK 800 producing 7500 amp hours. Us 46, 48-50, 52, 53-55, 74-76, 83-85, 87, 99-102: 2 x 62-cell AFA 33 MAL 800 W producing 9160 amp hours. Us 73, 86: 2 x 62-cell AFA 33 MAL 800 E producing 9160 amp hours
Boats of the type:	Us 45-55, 73-76, 83-87, 99-102
Builders:	Us 45-55, 69-72 (The last four boats were renumbered Us 99-102 after war broke out as part of a deception scheme to mislead the Allies and neutrals as to the actual strength of the U-boat arm) Germaniawerft, Kiel
	Us 73-76 Vegesacker Werft, Vegesack
	Us 83-87 Flender-Werft, Lübeck
Built:	1936 - 1940
Design:	As for the VII but 2 metres longer overall to accommodate more internal stores and the S-Geràt listening apparatus, and to increase fuel tank capacity both internally and externally. The length-to-beam ratio (external) was now decreased to 10.7:1 compared with 11:1 of the VII, despite the increase in length; it was due to the much increased capacity of the saddle-tanks which now had a capacity of 42.4 tons of fuel oil, compared with the 8.4 tons of the VII. Diving depth 100 metres; designed crush depth 200 metres. Diving time 30 seconds (normal)
Armament:	As the VII except that the stern (single) torpedo tube was now placed within the casing, and was loadable from the aft torpedo compartment, where one reserve torpedo was carried. The length increase in the pressure hull allowed for this practical modification, and for the increased torpedo carrying capacity, which was 14 torpedoes in all, or 26 TMA or 39 TMB mines. Torpedo stowage was now: 4 in forward tubes; 8 slung in forward torpedo compartment; 1 in aft tube; 1 in reserve in aft torpedo compartment. Some boats were able to carry more in external containers below the casing forward and aft, but this was often discontinued because of problems in shipping these torpedoes inboard, and the further problems caused by diving and surfacing, affecting the pressurised depth-keeping apparatus in the torpedo. Note that U 83 was not fitted with a stern torpedo tube. Guns as for the VII (in both cases, gun changes were made to those boats that survived into the latter half of the war; for a guide, assume the details were as for the VIIC)
Crew:	4 Officers, 44 ratings
Boats:	1 Dinghy, fitted as for VII
General:	The first modifications to the original form showed promise, and the 24 boats of this Type saw much service. U 47 was Prien's, and penetrated Scapa Flow. U 48 survived the war until scuttled in May 1945, having sunk more shipping than any other U-boat. Us 99 and 100 (Captains Kretschmer and Schepke) were very successful indeed, only to fall prey to the Royal Navy within sight of each other in March 1941)

TABLE 3: **THE TYPE VIIC**

Note that the majority of the Drawing Section deals with this Type except where otherwise stated; they comprised 94 per cent of the class, and so it is with their details that much of this work is concerned. Nevertheless, where possible, despite exigencies of space, the other types receive some consideration.

Displacement: Surface 719 tons (dry), 769 tons (water and fuel tanks full); submerged 871 tons (normal), 1070 tons (fully loaded)

Length overall: Casing 66.5 metres, pressure hull 50.5 metres
Beam: Casing 6.2 metres, pressure hull 4.7 metres
Keel to bridge overall: 9.6 metres
Draught (boat surfaced): 4.74 metres
Engines: As Type VIIB (Us 79-82, 90, 101, 102, 132-136 MAN, the remainder Germaniawerft diesels totalling 2800-3200bhp
Maximum revolutions 470-490rpm
Maximum surface speed 17-17.7 knots
Range 8500 sea miles at 10 knots; 3250 sea miles at 17.2 knots; combined diesel/electric drive range 9700 sea miles at 10 knots
Fuel oil maximum 113.5 tons; normal 105.3 tons, of which 62.1 tons within the pressure hull

Motors: Us 69-72, 89, 93-98, 201-212, 221-232, 235-300, 331-348, 351-374, 431-450, 731-750, 1051-1058, 1063, 1068, 1191-1214, 1271-1285, 1301-1312: 2 AEG GU 460/8-276 electric motors. Us 77-82, 88, 90-92, 99-100, 132-136, 401, 451, 452, 551-650, 751, 821-840, 929-936, 951-1050: 2 BBC (Brown Boveri and Co) GG UB 720/8 electric motors. Us 301-330, 375-400, 701-730, 752-782, 1131, 1132: 2 GL (Garbe, Lahmeyer) RP 137/c electric motors. Us 349, 350, 402-430, 453-458, 465-486, 651-698, 901-912, 921-928, 1101-1110, 1161-1170: 2 SSW (Siemens-Schuckert-Werke) GU 343/38-8 electric motors. Output totalled 750shp in all cases.
Maximum revolutions (geared down) 296rpm
Maximum submerged speed 7.6 knots
Range underwater 130 sea miles at 2 knots; 80 sea miles at 4 knots
Batteries Us 69-72, 77-80, 88-90, 93-95, 98, 99-102, 132, 133, 135, 136, 201-212, 221-226, 228-232, 238-240, 244, 245, 248, 251-255, 257-286, 291, 301-304, 306-313, 320, 328-345, 352-366, 372, 374, 376, 378-392, 401-404, 406, 408-412, 414-419, 421-425, 431-434, 436-440, 442-449, 451, 452, 454-458, 456, 466-472, 474, 551, 553, 556, 557, 559, 560, 562-571, 573-583, 585, 587-591, 594-599, 602-607, 609-617, 619-624, 626-638, 640, 642-668, 670-675, 682, 684-698, 701, 702, 710-713, 715-717, 720, 723-743, 751-757, 759-762, 764, 769-771, 777-782, 905, 907, 922, 951-957, 960, 963, 964, 967-994, 1053, 1104, 1131, 1133-1146, 1166, 1168, 1169, 1171, 1172, 1192, 1194, 1196-1199, 1201-1206, 1208, 1209, 1211-1214, 1272, 1306, 1331-1338, 1401-1404, 1417-1422, 1435-1439: 2 x 62-cell AFA 33 MAL 800 W producing 9160 amp hours. All other Type VIIC: 2 x 62-cell AFA 33 MAL 800 E (9160 amp hours) except for a small number of boats having combinations of series E and W type batteries (the difference was the casing of the individual battery cells).

Builders: **(Type VIIC):** Us 69-72, 99-102, 93-98, 201-212, 221-232, 235-250, 1051-1058, 1063-1065 Germaniawerft, Kiel
Us 77-82, 132-136, 251-291 Vegesacker Werft, Vegesack
Us 88-92, 301-316, 903-904 Flender-Werft, Lübeck
Us 331-350, 1101-1106 Nordsee-Werke, Emden
Us 351-370 Flensburger Schiffbau Gesellschaft, Flensburg
Us 371-400, 651-686, 1131-1132 Howaldtswerke, Kiel
Us 401-430, 1161, 1162 Danziger Werft, Danzig
Us 431-450, 731-750, 825-828, 1191-1210 F Schichau, Danzig
Us 451-486 Deutsche Werke, Kiel
Us 551-650, 951-994, 1007-1110 Blohm und Voss, Hamburg
Us 701-722, 905-908 H C Stülcken Sohn, Hamburg
Us 751-782 Kaiserliche Marinewerft, Wilhelmshaven
Us 821-824 Stettiner Orderwerke, Stettin
Us 901-902, (finishing work on Us 903-908) Stettiner Vulcan Werke, Stettin
Us 921-930 Neptun-Werft, Rostock
Builders (Type VIIC/41): Us 292-300, 1271-1279 Vegesacker Werft, Vegesack
Us 317-330 Flender-Werft, Lübeck
Us 687-698 Howaldtswerke, Hamburg
Us 723-730, 909-912 H C Stülcken, Hamburg

Us 829-840 F Schichau, Danzig
Us 931-936 Neptun-Werft, Rostock
Us 995-1006 Blohm und Voss, Hamburg
Us 1107 -1110 Nordsee-Werke, Emden
Us 1163-1170 Danziger Werft, Danzig
Us 1301-1308 Flensburger Schiffbau Gesellschaft, Flensburg

Built:
Design: 1938-1944
Once more there was an increase in fuel capacity by a slight increase in the overall size of the boat. Interestingly 5.6 per cent extra fuel capacity was achieved at a cost of only 1.6 per cent more displacement. Maximum speed remained about 17 knots, although the practical maximum was nearer 16 knots. The design for the boats was finalised in 1937-1938, and the only fundamental architectural change thereafter was the implementation of Ww grade steel in the VIIC/41 boats, listed above. The greatest variation came in armament and conning-towers (see below). The length-to-beam ratio was 10.7:1, as with the VIIB, for there was no increase in overall dimensions; the fuel increase came from enlarging the main midships fuel tanks.

Armament: The following boats had 2 forward torpedo tubes only: Us 72, 78, 80, 554, 555
The following boats had no stern torpedo tube: Us 203, 331, 351, 401, 431, 651
The following boats had no mine-carrying capability: Us 88-92, 333-350, 352-370, 374-401, 404-430, 435-450, 454-458, 657-686, 702-750, 754-782 and all boats Type C/41 from U1271 upwards
The 8.8cm was removed from many boats in 1942, and not included in requirements after that year. The threat of air attack was so great from 1943 onwards that additional and heavier calibre FlaK equipment began to appear on all boats. The bridge platform was increased in size by adding a lower platform to the one existing abaft the bridge itself, and the 'Wintergarten' concept of heavy anti-aircraft defence was brought into service. Gun types were generally the 2cm and 3.7cm FlaK cannon, in various combinations and permutations. There follow *some* of those variations:
  i: 1-2cm C30 on LC 30/37 mounting
  ii: 1-2cm C30 and 2 MG 151 machine guns (Mod I)
  iii: 2-2cm C30 on twin LC 30/37 (1 x 2) and 4 MG 151 machine guns (2 x 2)
  vi: 1-2cm C30 and 4 Breda machine guns (2 x 2; Mediterranean . modification of Us 81 and 453)
  v: Modification II - 2-2cm C38 (2 x 1), one on each level of the 'Wintergarten'
  vi: (Type VIID only, see below)
  vii: upper level 4-2cm C38 (2 x 2), lower level 4-2cm C38 and shield (1 x 4), or 1-3.7 cm automatic FlaK cannon
  viii: 1944-45 either 4-2cm C 38 M II on twin LM 42 U mounting (2 x 2) and 1-3.7cm M 42 U on LM 42 U mounting or instead of the 3.7cm weapon, 4-2cm FlaK 38/43 and shield (1 x 4), or 2-3.7cm M 42 on twin LM 42 U mounting (1 x 2)
There are many more variations, some official, some put together by the boats' captains. The majority of the time however, the best chance of survival lay in a constant air watch, and readiness to dive in an instant. The FlaK defences had little success after a few initial surprises.
A number of ECM sets were issued by the Germans to the U-boats, which met with varying degrees of success. A detailed discussion of them is not presented here, as they deserve a book in their own right. However some drawings show the various aerials, and the external appearance of the most common of the sets.

Crew: 4 officers, 56 ratings
General: 1. The various forms of the tower can be seen in elevation and plan in the Drawings Section.
2. Schnorchel. This was fitted as a standard equipment from mid-1944 onwards, with some boats having the equipment earlier. Essentially the Schnorchel was designed to get the boats into their operational areas as quickly as possible with the minimum danger. This meant that the diesels could be used to propel the boats, and the batteries were maintained at full charge, so that the boats could escape air or surface attack by going deeper. They could make good a fast escape, then return to Schnorchel depth and resume their course. With only the head of the raised inlet/exhaust arm showing above the water, the boats had

a better chance than on the surface. 3cm radar, developed in the United States, eventually limited even this method of maintaining the offensive.

3. The main additions to the VIIB that typify the VIIC are as follows:

a. The tower was enlarged by 30cm in length and 6cm in width, giving slightly more room on the bridge, and improving the underwater contour of the tower

b. Improvement of the diving characteristics by installing a pressure-tight diving tank (port and starboard) forward of the regulating tanks

c. As noted above, increasing fuel tank Ii by 5.4 cubic metres

d. Improvements in oil-cleaning equipment to increase engine performance

e. Improvements in electric switching

f. The provision of four canisters in the fore casing, each holding a 5 man inflatable life raft

Note: Drawings of the Type VIIC/42 boat have not been included as none were built. It was to have had a stronger hull (designed operational diving depth 280 metres; designed crush depth 400 metres), but only got as far as the design stage.

TABLE 4: **THE TYPE VIID**

Note that this boat was designed to fulfil a dual role, as both a minelayer and a torpedo-carrying boat

Displacement:	Surface (dry) 919 tons, normal 965 tons; submerged 1080 – 1285 tons depending upon armament carried
Length overall:	Casing 76.9 metres, pressure hull 59.8 metres
Beam:	Casing 6.38 metres, pressure hull 4.7 metres
Keel to bridge overall:	9.7 metres
Draught (boat surfaced):	5.01 metres
Engines:	2 Germaniawerft 6-cylinder 4-stroke F 46 diesels with superchargers totalling 2800-3200bhp
	Maximum revolutions 470-490rpm
	Maximum speed 16-16.7 knots
	Range 11,200 sea miles at 10 knots; 5050 sea miles at 16 knots; combined diesel/electric drive range 13,000 sea miles at 10 knots
	Fuel oil maximum 169.4 tons; normal 155.2 tons, of which 115.3 tons within the pressure hull
Motors:	2 AEG GU 460/8-276 electric motors totalling 750shp
	Maximum revolutions (geared down) 285rpm
	Maximum submerged speed 7.3 knots
	Range underwater 127 sea miles at 2 knots; 69 sea miles at 4 knots
	Batteries: 2 x 62-cell AFA 33 MAL 800 E cells producing 9160 amp hours (U 217 W type cells)
Builder:	Us 213-218 Germaniawerft, Kiel.
Built:	1940-1942
Designed:	The design was completed in 1939–40 to fill the need for more minelaying craft which could be easily built. The Type IX and X boats soon took over this role however, and only these 6 boats were built. They were identical to the standard Type VIIC with the exception that between frames 39 and 40 (aft of the tower) a 9.8-metre insert was built in. This contained five vertical unpressurised mine shafts, each holding three SMA mines. The extension of the main hull meant that the saddle-tanks could also be extended, and this led to the increased fuel capacity. Extra ballast and diving tanks could also be incorporated. Diving depth 100 metres; designed crush depth 200 metres. The twin rudders and the hydroplanes were as fitted to the VIIC. A Schnorchel was carried on the port side of the tower.
Armament:	5-53.3cm (4 forward and 1 stern) torpedo tubes; 12 torpedoes or 26 TMA or 39 TMB mines could be carried, as well as 15 SMA mines in the midships mine shafts
	1 - 8.8cm C35 L/45 main deck gun with 220 rounds of ammunition
	2 - 2cm FlaK cannon C30 (2 x 1) with 4380 rounds of ammunition
	After 1942 defensive armament changed to:
	1 - 3.7 FlaK with 1195 rounds of ammunition
	4 - 2cm C38 (2 x 2) with 4380 rounds of ammunition
Crew:	4 Officers and 40 ratings
Boats:	1 dinghy
General:	The normal FlaK balcony aft of the bridge was widened rather than lengthened in the VIID so that it did not overhang the forward mine shaft. The boat was a stop-gap, and nothing more; only one survived the war, to be sunk in Operation 'Deadlight' (the post-war Royal Navy operation that scuttled the surrendered U-boats not required for evaluation and experiments)
Note:	Little is known of the Type VIIE design, except that it was for a boat with an uprated engine. It got no further than design sketches.

TABLE 5: **THE TYPE VIIF**

Displacement:	Surface 1084 tons; submerged (dry) 1181 tons, (fully loaded and manned) 1345 tons
Length overall:	Casing 77.63 metres, pressure hull 60.4 metres
Beam:	Casing 7.3 metres, pressure hull 4.7 metres
Keel to bridge overall:	9.6 metres
Draught (boat surfaced)	4.7 metres
Engines:	2 Germaniawerft 6-cylinder 4-stroke F 46 diesel totalling 2880-3200bhp at 470-490rpm
	Maximum surface speed 16.9-17.6 knots
	Range 14,700 sea miles at 10 knots; 5350 sea miles at 16.9 knots; combined diesel/electric drive range 13,950 sea miles at 10 knots
	Fuel oil 198.8 tons
Motors:	2 AEG GU 460/8-276 electric motors totalling 750shp
	Maximum revolutions (geared down) 295rpm
	Maximum submerged speed 7.9 knots
	Range underwater 130 sea miles at 2 knots; 75 sea miles at 4 knots
	Batteries 2 x 62-cell AFA 33 MAL 800 E (U 1059 W type) producing 9160 amp hours
Builder:	Us 1059-1062 Germaniawerft, Kiel.
Built:	1941-1943
Designed:	The design, based on the VIIC, was completed in 1941; they were conceived as both fighting boats and supply vessels. The torpedo compartment added (in a similar manner to the VIID) was for either the boat's own use, or for re-supplying boats in operational areas which had adequate fuel, but were short of torpedoes. By the time they came into service (March 1943), the day of the U-boat was past, and they served solely as fighting boats. They had a Schnorchel on the port side of the tower, the VIIC's rudder arrangement, and diving time was about 35 seconds. Only U 1061 survived, being sunk in Operation 'Deadlight'.
Armament:	5-53.3cm (4 forward, 1 stern) torpedo tubes. The normal inboard 14 torpedoes were carried to fight the ship. No mine capability. Up to 21 torpedoes could be carried in the torpedo cargo room; 2 further torpedoes could be stowed in watertight containers either side and aft of the tower
	1 - 3.7cm with 1195 rounds of ammunition
	2 - 2cm C38 with 4380 rounds of ammunition
Crew:	4 officers, 42 ratings
Boats:	1 dinghy
General:	As with the VIID this hybrid design suffered from other more suitable designs taking its place, and from the general situation in the battle areas. It was a stop-gap design that had no valid role by the time it was completed.

TABLE 6: **GERMAN SUBMARINE TORPEDOES**

Type		Propulsion	Range/speed	Notes
G7a	T1	Compressed air (wet heater)	6000m/44kts 800m/40kts 14,000m/30kts	The pre-war issue torpedo, it had the disadvantage of leaving a visible trail of bubbles on its way to the target.
G7e	T2	Electric	5000m/30kts	The standard torpedo of the war. It suffered from early problems with its internal depth-keeping equipment, and its firing pistol, but these were solved after a Board of Enquiry following the Norwegian Campaign.
	T3	Electric	5000m/30kts	As for the T2 but fitted with an influence fuse
	T4	Electric	7500m/20kts	The first homing torpedo, fitted with a passive acoustic homing device, but very few were used.
	T5	Electric	5700m/24kts	The 'Zaunkönig' ('Gnat'). Intended to be an escort killer, it achieved some minor early success only to be countered by the 'Foxer' noise-making decoy.
	T11	Electric	5700m/24kts	A modified T5, less affected by 'Foxer'. Never used in battle conditions, although late test results were promising.

Notes: All the above were 53.3cm (21-inch) torpedoes. There were also two important pattern-running devices which could be applied to various torpedo types. These were 'FAT' and 'LUT'. 'FAT' ran a wandering course with regular 180° turns, was useful against convoys, and was fitted to both G7a and to G7e T3s. 'LUT' was more sophisticated with more variable patterns, but was only used operationally towards the end of the war.

TABLE 7: **U-BOAT GUNS AND MOUNTINGS**

Type	Notes
7.92mm MG C34	The naval version of the standard German infantry machine gun. The rate of fire was c1000rpm, but the weapon was ineffective against aircraft.
2cm MG C30	The first of a number of 20mm weapons fitted to the U-boats. it was normally mounted as a single weapon, and could be operated by two men. Rate of fire was 280-300rpm. Watertight canister mount, or free-swinging single or twin LC 30/27 mountings.
2cm FlaK 38	This was an enhanced version of the MG C30, with an increased rate of fire (450-500rpm). It was mounted initially as for the C30, but there were also more advanced LM 43 U (*Flak-Zwilling*) twin mounts and the quadruple L 38/43 U (*Flak-Vierling*).
3.7cm SKC30U	The first larger calibre FlaK issued to the U-boats. This version was manually loaded, and had a rate of fire of approximately 30rpm. Later versions were automated. Fitted on a single LC 39 mounting.
3.7cm FlaK M42U	An automatic gun, based on the army's Flak 36, capable of 160-180rpm. It was mounted late in the war on LM 42 U single and twin mountings.
8.8cm SKC35	The naval version of the army 'eighty-eight', but ammunition was not interchangeable. This 45-cal gun was intended for use as auxiliary armament, and often used to sink small craft, or administer the *coup de grâce* to vessels not worth another torpedo. Fitted on hand-worked single LC 35 mountings.

Note: German gun designations can be confusing.'SKC' denotes 'ship gun', followed by two numbers denoting the normal year of development (ie omitting the 19–). This is often shortened to just 'C' and the year. A 'U' (for 'U-boat') was added to designate a submarine gun or mounting, and 'FlaK' was sometimes included with AA guns. From early in the war the prefix became 'KM', or 'FlaK M' and the date. Mountings were prefixed by 'LC', and later 'LM', or simply 'L', followed by the date (as for guns). In common usage, almost all these designations were regularly shortened.

The Photographs

1. *U 98* shortly before she was launched. A Type VIIC boat, the lines of her bow and the forward outer casing can be seen clearly. She took eleven months to build. The tower is of the standard type, with which the Type VII boats were generally fitted until 1943. On the left, at an early stage of building, is the pressure hull of *U 208*. Both boats were built by Germaniawerft at Kiel, on Slip 4.

2. This stern view of a Type VIIC boat shows the fineness of the lines aft of the conning tower. The twin rudders are most noticeable. Her number is not known, but it is clear that she has been commissioned, because the *Reichskriegsflagge* is flying at the ensign staff. She has probably been into dry dock for modification or repair.

3. This photograph also depicts a Type VIIC boat, lying at anchor after launch. She flies no flag, and has no armament fitted so must be awaiting a move to a finishing dock. The port saddle-tank, and (below, forward) the pressure hull can be seen, as well as the characteristic drainage slots of this type.

4. The Type VIIC *U 570* was the first U-boat to be captured intact, when she surrendered to two Hudson aircraft of Coastal Command on 4 October 1941. Seen here in a British port under the White Ensign, she was later commissioned for evaluation as HMS *Graph*.
Conway Picture Library.

5. *U 218*, a Type VIID, after she was launched at Krupp's Germaniawerft in Kiel, on 5 December 1941. She has completed her training period with the 5th U-boat Flotilla, and is back in Kiel for fitting out before joining her operational flotilla (the 9th) in Brest, which she did in September 1942. She survived the war, and at the end of hostilities was in Bergen. She sailed from there and was scuttled by the Royal Navy in Operation 'Deadlight'. The photograph also shows *U 226* and *U 227* (both Type VIIC) and enables some comparison of the respective sizes of boats to be made.

6. A Type VIIC boat at sea in the Baltic. Casing hatches fore and aft of the tower are open, the harbour rails are fitted, and two crew members are seen on the aft FlaK platform – the only place for a cigarette. The boat was probably based in the Baltic and used for training purposes.

7. Another of the trick-numbered U-boats, *U 100*, which was originally *U 70*. This near-silhouette, taken late in the afternoon, shows the forward casing draining slots and the bridge outline.

8. This camouflaged boat is *U 617*. Launched and commissioned in 1942, she had the doubtful honour of being transferred into the Mediterranean as a result of the Allied landings in North Africa. The camouflage pattern did her no great service, and she was lost on 12 September 1943. First attacked by aircraft of 179 Squadron RAF, she was beached by orders of her Captain, KL Brandi. Then she was destroyed where she lay by the combined gunfire of HM Ships *Hyacinth* and *Haarlem* and HMAS *Wollongong*.

9. Although the boat in the photograph is a Type II (*U 14*), the torpedo is a standard G7a weapon, which was the basic torpedo of the *Kriegsmarine*, until the G7e was issued, the latter being propelled by electric motors as opposed to compressed air.

10

11

10. This is a breech view of the standard main deck gun, the 8.8cm C35 L/45. The 8.8cm saw service elsewhere, notably as an anti-aircraft and anti-tank gun, and in the German Navy was used by the U-boats for attacks on small vessels, and to administer the *coup de grâce* to larger targets. Such use of deck guns was possible in the first half of the war, and saved many torpedoes; later they were all removed due to the dangers of surface operation. This gun had no anti-aircraft facility, being designed solely for surface-to-surface gunnery.

11. The Captain and First Lieutenant at the periscope. (The Captain *may* be K Kapt Georg Lassen, who survived the war.) The periscope viewing base is quite clear, as is the angle setter (marked –10 to +20 degrees). To the left of the picture is the eyepiece for reading the bearing angle to target. This is the control room periscope, which eventually became the air-search periscope.

12. The diesel engine compartment. On either side of the photograph stand the 6-cylinder diesel engines, and the vertical rods are the engine valve operating arms. At the top of the picture, which shows the view aft, is the control wheel for the engine room air intake trunking (closed when diving). In the centre of the photograph is the watertight door to the Motor Room, and two revolution counters can be seen as well as the central fuel indicator gauge. On the upper part of the picture are two fume extractors, either side of the fuel gravity tank.

13

12

14

15

13. This photograph shows the forward torpedo compartment. The four inner tube doors can be seen, with a G7e torpedo slung in the loading position for Tube II. On the forward bulkhead is the main firing control panel, which is of interest because it is the 'LUT' (see Table 6) firing board. The air pipe from the torpedo compressed air cartridge to Tube IV is clearly visible as well as the (black painted) flooding tube, which led from the Tube via the control valve to the torpedo flooding tank.

14. This view shows the forward watertight bulkhead opening (leading forward to the officers' quarters).

15. *U 552* returning to base after a successful patrol. KL Topp is seen on the port side of the bridge, with his First Lieutenant by the attack periscope housing. The watchman on the fore bridge is calling engine orders to the control room via the voice pipe. The small flags record the sinkings during each patrol the boat made, and *U 552* and Topp were together from December 1940 until August 1942. The running devil motif on the bridge casing was one of many that appeared early in the war, but were largely dispensed with later on when the Allied successes against the U-boats removed any light-heartedness there had been among the crews.

16. The commissioning of *U 201* on 25 January 1941. KL Schnee, the Captain is looking aft on the port side of the bridge. He was just 27 at the time, and had already commanded *U*s 6 and 60. The boat's shield is seen above the wave deflector. *U 201*, unlike Captain Schnee, did not survive the war, being lost (under another commander) in February 1943 to depth charges from HMS *Fame* off Newfoundland.

17. A meeting between *U 826* and *U 236* (both Type VIICs) after the end of the war. All armament has been removed, they both fly the White Ensign, and the hats of many of the crew of the righthand boat are certainly Royal Navy issue. The crew members on the forward casing of the docking boat are German Navy, no doubt impressed to sail the boat to Loch Ryan for Operation 'Deadlight'. The Schnorchel inlet on the port side of the tower casing is most visible in the righthand boat, while the other boat shows off her 'Wintergarten' railing very well.

18. A bow outer casing section en route to the final assembly yard. With the advent of the so-called strategic bombing offensive the German Navy decided wherever possible to prefabricate both outer casing sections and pressure hull segments. This was also aimed at cutting the amount of time the boats were lying on the stocks, vulnerable to bombing (which was rarely that effective).

19. Starboard view of *U 441* (*U FlaK 1*). The quadruple 2cm mountings were visible fore and aft of the bridge, as well as the aerial for the FuMO 61.

20. The attack persicope standard. Hanging on its side is a signal lamp, and a pair of Zeiss binoculars can be seen mounted on the fore bridge on a pelorus. The boat is in harbour and the crew is enjoying a smoke break. The boat is *U 99*, a Type VIIB (see also Frontispiece). She was lost in 1941 to the depth charges of HMS *Walker*, south east of Iceland.

21. This stern view of *U 1168*, taken in 1945, shows the whole of the 'Wintergarten' aft of the bridge. In the background are the twin 2cm mountings, and in the foreground the twin 3.7cm FlaK and shield.

22. Launched in July 1944, *U 1305* was eventually taken by the Russians as war booty, and commissioned in the Soviet Navy as *S 84* until she was broken up in 1963. The life raft containers are visible on the bow casing, and the general silhouette is quite clear. From the attitude of the gunner at the 20mm Oerlikon in the foreground, as well as the 3.7cm FlaK barrel angle, it seems that this picture was taken as she surfaced to surrender.

23. Another, better, view of the 'Wintergarten' as Us 190 and 889 lie alongside after surrender. The twin 3.7cm mounting is particularly clear on the far boat, as are the twin 2cm fittings nearer the bridge. The casing for the FuMO 61 is also visible.

24. The last voyage: a Type VIIC (1944 equipment) is seen sailing to be scuttled by a scratch Royal Navy crew during Operation 'Deadlight'.
All uncredited photographs BfZ.

The Drawings

A NOTE ON THE DRAWINGS

The drawings are arranged on a thematic basis. They start on the outside of the boat, and then show in a series of more detailed drawings the internal arrangements of the major variants of the Type VII design. These drawings are followed in turn by even more detailed presentations of the compartments into which structurally the boats were divided. These compartments were the result of both naval and building requirements, and each is shown in considerable detail. There are also a number of perspective drawings of the interior and exterior of the boats – drawings done with the modeller specifically in mind.

There are also a number of drawings showing weapons (guns and torpedoes in particular). As noted above, the towers of the Type VII boats underwent a considerable number of changes, and even the *official* list includes seven main modifications. Considerable space is devoted to these, as the tower was the most easily recognisable part of these boats when they were surfaced.

Almost all of the basic drawings have been taken from original plans, or from drawings made after the war, in themselves taken from German originals. Many of the other drawings have been done after detailed research into photographs of actual boats. Further drawings (marked as *U 995*) were done after the author's research in Laboë and Hamburg. The reader may like to know that *U 995* is preserved as a memorial to the German U-boat Arm at Laboë, some 18 kilometres from Kiel. She is well worth a visit, the results of which will reward anyone interested in the subject, and armed with a plentiful supply of film and flash bulbs.

Most drawings are scaled to 1/200 or 1/100, with the exception of the perspectives and details which are produced at a scale to give maximum clarity.

A General arrangement – external

A1 TYPE VIIC AS IN 1936 (the boat is as rigged for harbour)

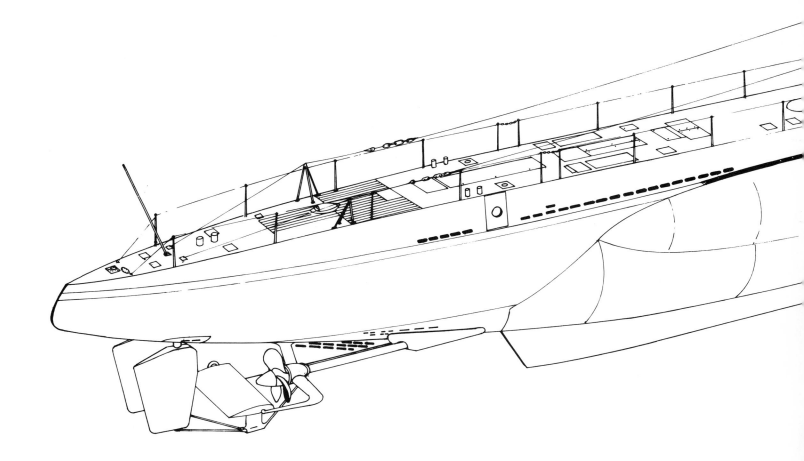

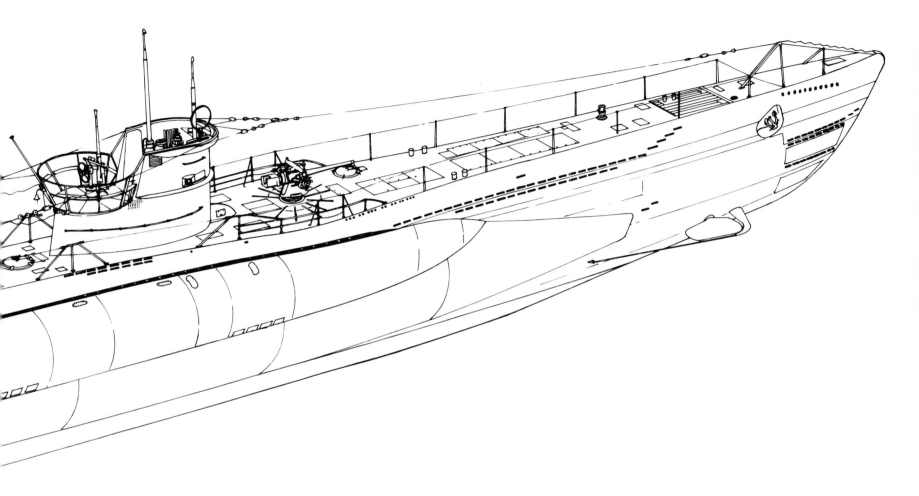

A General arrangement – external

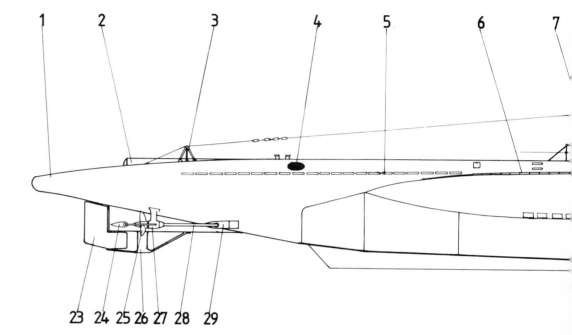

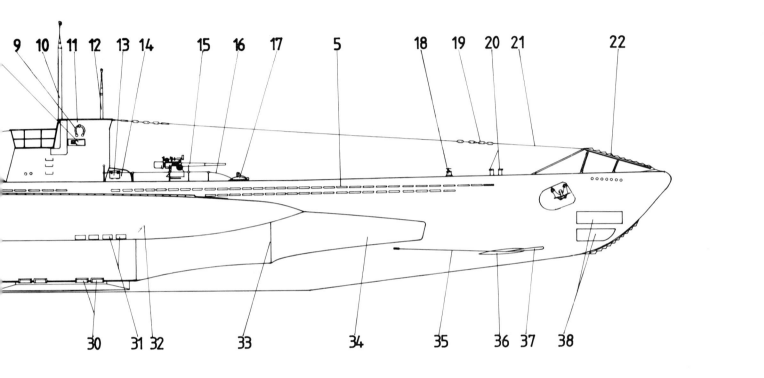

9 10 11 12 13 14 15 16 17 5 18 19 20 21 22

30 31 32 33 34 35 36 37 38 **A 2**

29

A General arrangement – external

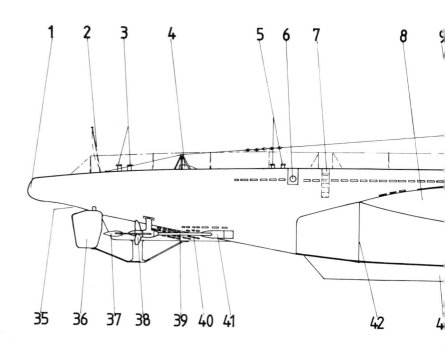

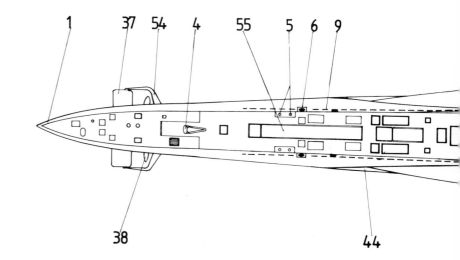

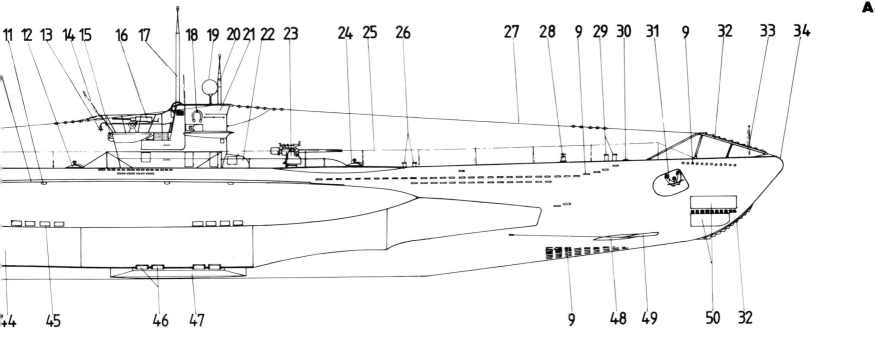

11 12 13 14 15   16 17   18 19 20 21 22 23   24 25   26   27   28   9 29 30 31   9   32   33   34

+4   45   46   47   9   48 49   50 32

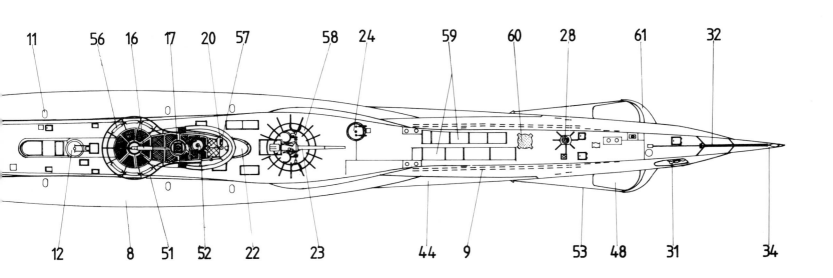

11   56 16   17   20   57   58   24   59   60   28   61   32

12   8   51   52   22   23   44   9   53   48   31   34

A General arrangement – external

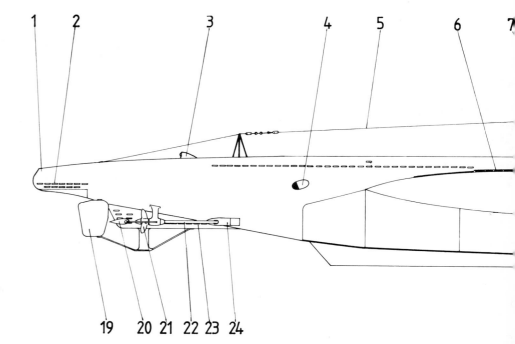

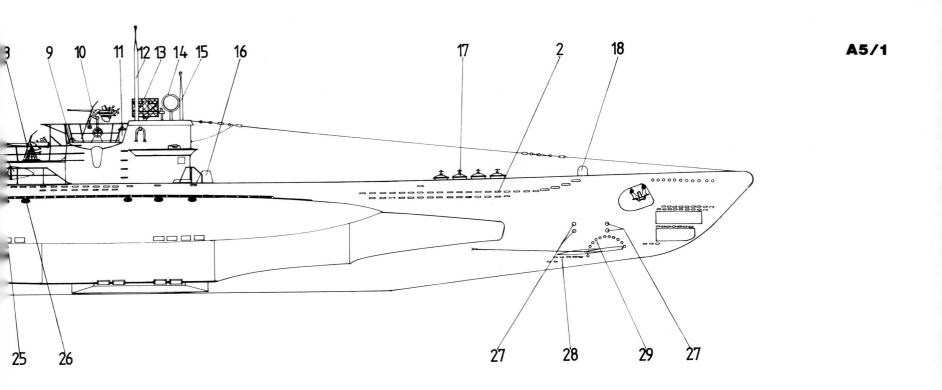

A5/1

A General arrangement – external

A5/2 TYPE VIIC/41 (elevation)
This drawing shows *U 995* as she appeared in the last two years of the war, when she operated on the Arctic Front. In the last year of the war she was fitted with the *Balkon Gerät*, which can be seen below her bow; this was yet one more German attempt to upgrade sound location for the U-boats to allow them to find their targets, the convoys. Once more, although sophisticated, this equipment came too late and in far too small numbers to have any effect on the overall conduct of the war.

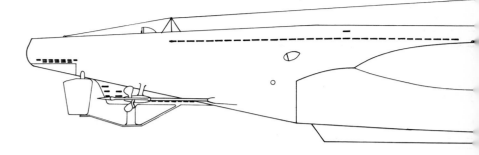

A5/3 TYPE VIIC/41 (deck plan)
This plan shows the enlarged tower, made necessary by the extra FlaK installations on the upper and lower '*Wintergarten*', as well as the wooden decking. This became a more frequent item on the U-boats as the war progressed, for German steel requirements were such that economies had to be made – and U-boat decks were one of these economies.

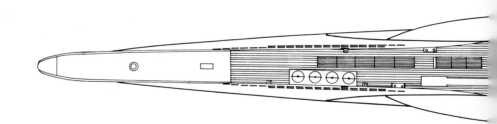

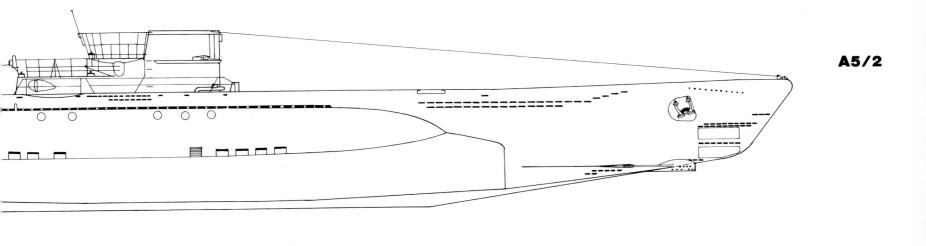

A5/2

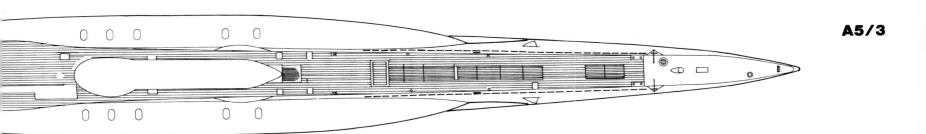

A5/3

A General arrangement – external

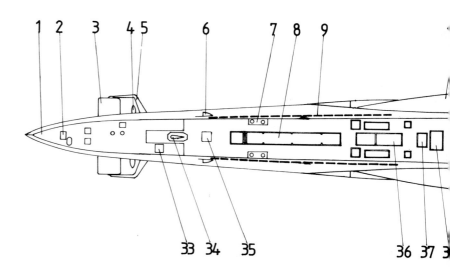

A6/2

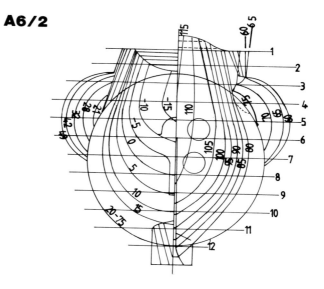

11 12 13 14 15 16 17 18 19 20 21 22 23 24 25 26 27 28 29 30 31 32

A6/1

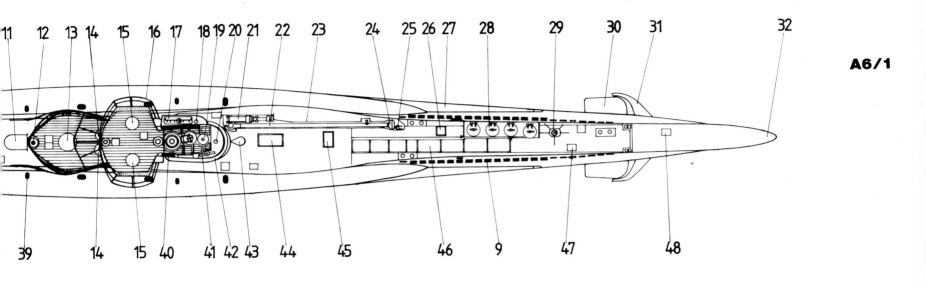

39 14 15 40 41 42 43 44 45 46 9 47 48

A General arrangement – external

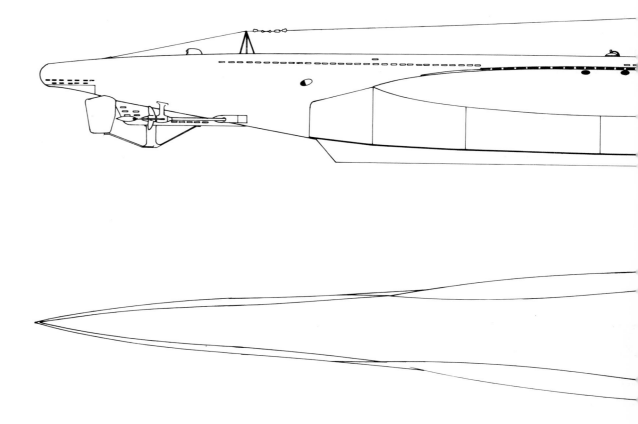

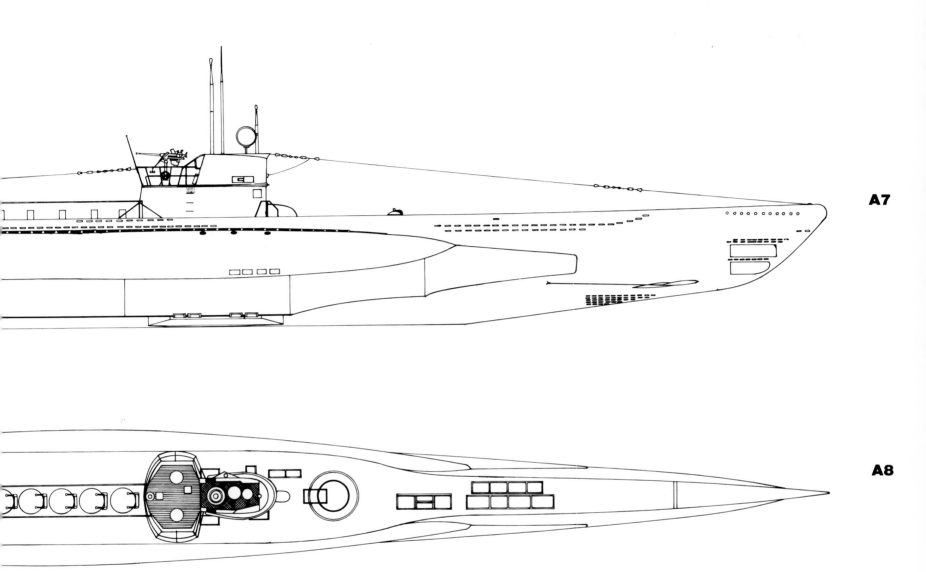

A7

A8

A General arrangement – external

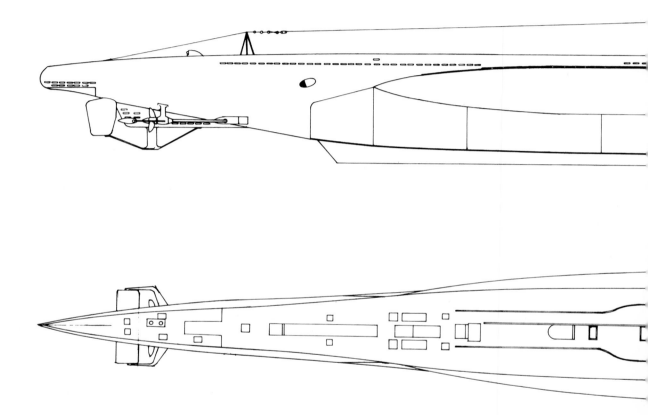

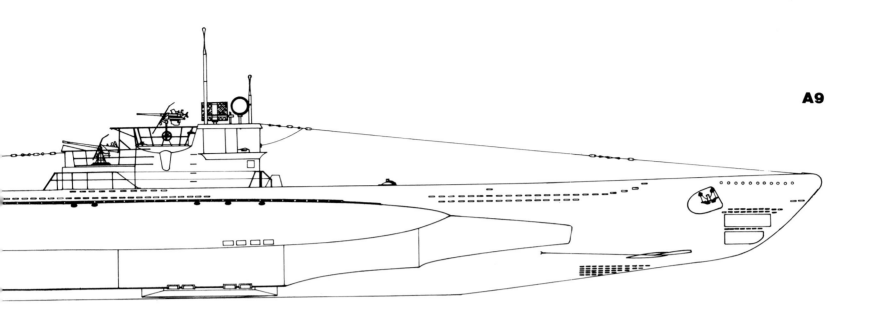

A9

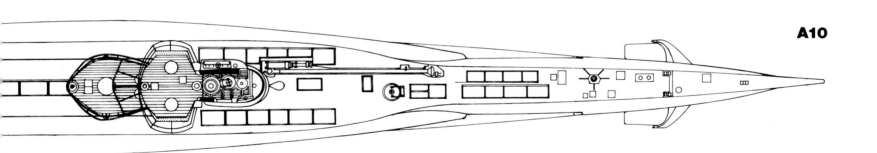

A10

A General arrangement – external

**A11   FLOODING SLOTS, OUTER
CASING DECK (Type VIIB, 1940)**

A12	VARIATIONS IN BRIDGE LAYOUT AND ARMAMENT	A12/3	TYPE VIIB (1940)
		1	Deck of outer casing
		2	Access escape hatch (to galley)
A12/1	**ORIGINAL FORM (Types VII and VIIB, 1936–39)**	3	Boat's bell
		4	Ensign staff
1	Radio aerial	5	Gun platform railing (fixed)
2	Insulators	6	2cm C30 FlaK
3	Boat's bell	7	Attack periscope
4	Ensign staff	8	Signalling mast
5	Platform guard rail	9	Air intake (meshed)
6	Attack periscope	10	DF aerial
7	Bridge casing	11	Control room periscope
8	Control room periscope	12	Life belt
9	Block and tackle	13	Starboard navigation light
10	Deck (outer casing)	14	Aerial insulators
11	2cm C30 FlaK	15	Bridge after navigation light
12	Ready-use ammunition container (watertight)	16	Access/inspection hatch to diesel air trunking and masts
13	Access hatch to exhausts/air intakes for diesels and engine room	17	Drainage holes (bridge and gun platform)
14	Access hatches to tower casing	18	Bridge access steps
15	Main compass housing	19	Access hatches to tower casing
16	Access hatches to compass housing	20	Main magnetic compass housing
17	8.8cm C35 deck gun	21	Access hatch to magnetic compass
18	Fixed casing rail	22	Wave deflector
19	Dismountable safety wire	23	8.8cm C35 deck gun
		24	Watertight 8.8cm ready-use ammunition container

A12/2   ORIGINAL FORM (general view; no scale)
The Type VII bridge illustrates the simple lines of the early tower. This drawing should be compared with the view of the Type VIIC/41 (A12/12).

A12/4   TYPE VIIB (general view looking forward; no scale)

1	Safety rail
2	Lookout stand
3	Bridge engine revolution repeater
4	Compass repeater
5	UZO (*Unterseeboots Ziel Ortungsgerät* – submarine target sight) base
6	Voice pipe to control room
7	Attack periscope housing
8	DF aerial housing
9	Air inlet trunking
10	2cm FlaK pedestal

A12/1

A12/2

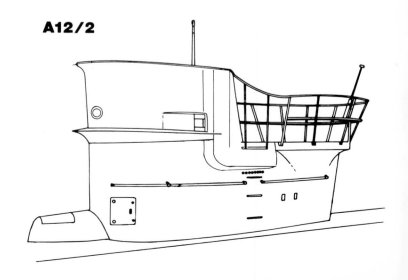

A11

A12/3

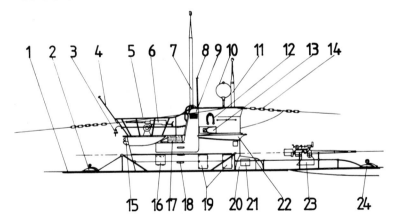

1 2 3 4 5 6 7 8 9 10 11 12 13 14

15 16 17 18 19 20 21 22 23 24

A12/4

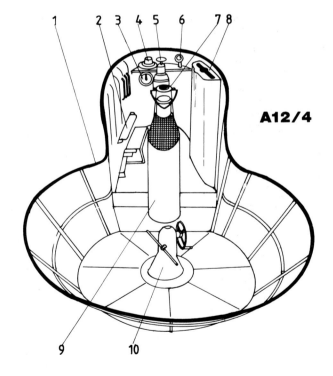

1 2 3 4 5 6 7 8

9 10

A General arrangement – external

A12/5

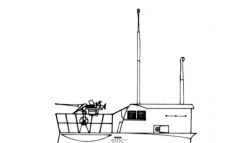

A12/6

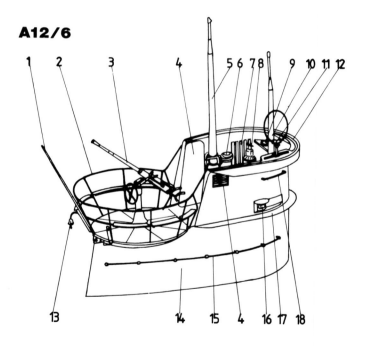

1 2 3 4 5 6 7 8 9 10 11 12

13 14 15 4 16 17 18

A12/7

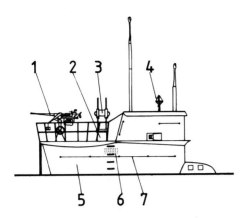

A12/9

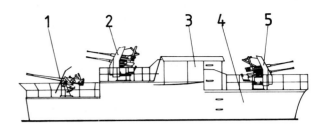

A12/8

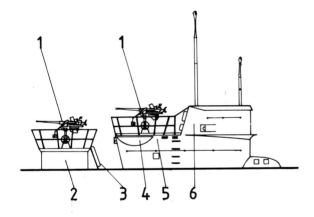

A12/10

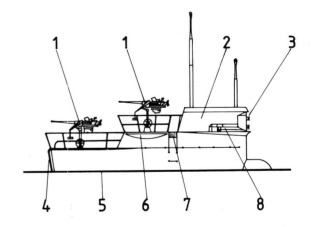

A General arrangement – external

A12/11 TYPE VIIC (1944–45)
1 3.7cm watertight ready-use ammunition container
2 3.7cm SKC30U on LC 39 mounting
3 2cm watertight ready-use ammunition container
4 2cm C38 twin LM 43 U FlaK cannon and shield (port and starboard)
5 Main 2cm watertight ready-use ammunition container
6 Aerial for FuMO 61 and DF set
7 Attack periscope
8 Aerial for FuMB 26
9 Air search periscope
10 Armoured bridge casing (splinter-proof)
11 Outer casing deck
12 Access ladder to lower gun platform
13 Fixed guard rails
14 Hand rail
15 Upper gun platform support
16 Drainage holes (bridge and upper gun platform)
17 Improved wave deflector

A12/12 TYPE VIIC/41 (general view with Schnorchel raised and lower 'Wintergarten'; no scale)
1 Main magnetic compass
2 Control room periscope
3 DF aerial
4 Attack periscope
5 'Bali' aerial (FuMB 29)
6 Air inlet trunking
7 2cm ready-use ammunition container
8 Two 2cm FlaK
9 Upper 'Wintergarten'
10 Safety rail (to prevent guns firing at dangerous angles)
11 3.7cm automatic FlaK
12 Schnorchel housing
13 Schnorchel piston
14 Schnorchel (with a second 'Bali' aerial at its head)
15 Housing and aerial of radar equipment
16 Access steps
17 Lower 'Wintergarten'
18 5 man life raft container

A12/13 TYPE VIIC/41 (U 995, elevation)
1 3.7cm FlaK
2 Position of gun shield when folded forward
3 Gun shield
4 Gun cradle
5 Feed guides for 5-round ammunition clips
6 Twin 2cm FlaK (port and starboard)
7 Gun shield
8 Upper 'Wintergarten' safety railings
9 Line of conning tower
10 Ventilator
11 Attack periscope self-greasing liner
12 UZO binoculars
13 Control room/air search periscope and self-greasing liner
14 Stern navigation light
15 Ready-use ammunition container (watertight) for 3.7cm ammunition
16 Lower 'Wintergarten'
17 Training pedestal for 3.7cm FlaK
18 3.7cm FlaK base
19 Gunlayer's seat
20 Training wheel
21 Safety rail
22 2cm ready-use ammunition container (watertight)
23 Upper 'Wintergarten' support
24 2cm FlaK pedestal
25 Immediate-use 2cm ammunition container (watertight)
26 Attack periscope
27 Outer casing
28 UZO pedestal and computer transmitter
29 Control room/air search periscope
30 Forward line of conning tower casing

A12/14 TYPE VIIC/41 (U 995, forward elevation, showing the asymmetrical aspect of the conning tower in the latter years of the war)
1 Upper wave deflector
2 Upper 'Wintergarten' safety railing
3 Schnorchel locking housing and air input trunking port
4 Starboard navigation light
5 Lower 'Wintergarten' and safety railing
6 Main magnetic compass housing
7 Low pressure air outlet piping to Schnorchel

A12/11

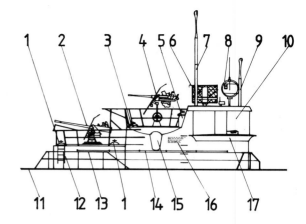

A12/12

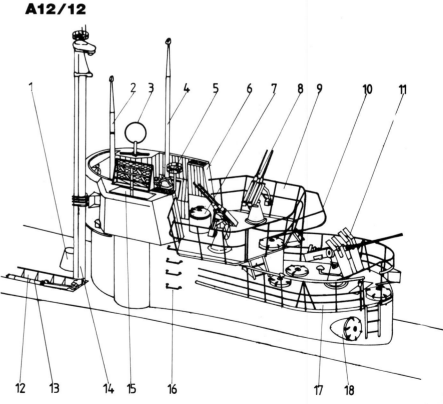

A12/13

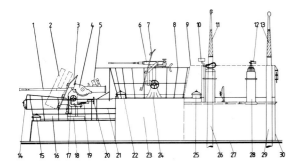

A12/15

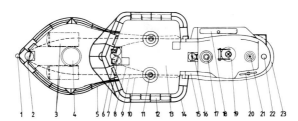

A12/14

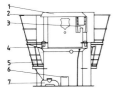

A12/16

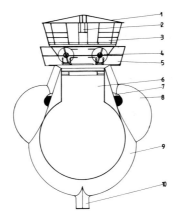

A12/15 TYPE VIIC/41 (*U 995*, plan view)

1 Stern navigation light
2 Ready-use ammunition container (watertight) for 3.7cm
3 Watertight container for 5 man raft
4 3.7cm gun mounting pedestal
5 Lower '*Wintergarten*' railing
6 Access ladder to upper '*Wintergarten*'
7 Ready-use ammunition container (two) for 2cm weapons
8 Line of upper '*Wintergarten*'
9 General outline of extended bridge
10 Outline of railing extension for lower '*Wintergarten*'
11 Mounting for two 2cm mountings
12 Seats for crew
13 Upper '*Wintergarten*' deck
14 Upper '*Wintergarten*' safety railing
15 Air inlet (port and starboard) for diesel air intakes
16 Ready-use ammunition locker (first use) for 2cm weapons
17 Attack periscope sleeve
18 Housing for radar aerials
19 Attack tower access/escape hatch
20 DF aerial and housing
21 UZO mounting and sleeve
22 Control room periscope sleeve and housing
23 Forward (upper) wave deflector

A12/16 TYPE VIIC/41 (*U 995*, view from aft)

1 Safety rail of upper '*Wintergarten*'
2 Attack periscope
3 Upper '*Wintergarten*'
4 5 man life raft containers (watertight)
5 Lower '*Wintergarten*'
6 Lower '*Wintergarten*' support
7 Starboard diesel exhaust
8 Starboard saddle tank
9 Outer casing line abaft the tower
10 Keel

B General arrangements – internal

B1/1 INTERNAL PROFILE, TYPE VII
1 Stern casing
2 Stern diving tank
3 Stern external torpedo tube (I)
4 Electric motor room
5 Diesel engine compartment
6 Galley
7 Galley access/escape hatch (watertight)
8 Hardened pedestal for 2cm FlaK mounting
9 Senior rates' mess
10 Aft casing of tower
11 Attack periscope and sheath
12 Control room periscope
13 Bridge casing
14 Attack centre
15 Access hatch between attack centre and control room (with bridge watertight hatch above)
16 Main magnetic compass and housing
17 Hardened pedestal for 8.8cm main deck gun mounting
18 Captain's cabin
19 Officers' quarters and wardroom
20 Chief rates' mess
21 Forward torpedo loading hatch
22 Forward torpedo room and ratings' quarters
23 Torpedo tube II (one of four)
24 Bow diving tank
25 Anchor chain locker (free-flooding)
26 Watertight bow section
27 Bow casing
28 Single rudder
29 Rudder and hydroplane support beam
30 Free-flooding after casing
31 Torpedo compensating tank, aft torpedo tube
32 Aft trim tank
33 Electric motor mounting
34 Diesel engine mounting
35 Lower engine room space
36 Fresh water tank
37 Battery compartment floor mounting
38 Battery room I
39 Keel
40 Fuel oil tank
41 Attack periscope sleeve
42 Main diving tank
43 Control room periscope sleeve
44 Fuel oil tank
45 Internal deck plating
46 Battery room II
47 Forward torpedo compensating tank (port and starboard, each serving two tubes)
48 Forward trim tank
49 Reserve torpedo storage space

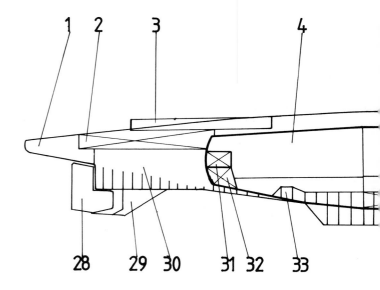

B1/2 INTERNAL PLAN VIEW, TYPE VII
1 Stern hydroplane and rudder support beam
2 Free-flooding after casing
3 Aft torpedo tube compensating tank
4 Motor room
5 Engine room
6 Galley
7 Fuel oil tank
8 Saddle-tank ballast cell (port and starboard)
9 Fuel/water compensation tank (port and starboard)
9a Fresh water tank (linked to control system of 9)
10 Forward battery automatic switching room
11 Captain's cabin
12 Fuel oil tank
13 Forward torpedo room and ratings' quarters
14 Bow torpedo tubes (number I to starboard, number II to port)
15 Bow diving tank
16 After battery automatic switching room
17 'Heads' (lavatories)
18 Senior rates' quarters and mess
19 Attack periscope sleeve
20 Control room periscope sleeve
21 Radio room
22 Wardroom
23 Food store
24 Heads and washroom
25 Chief rates' mess and quarters

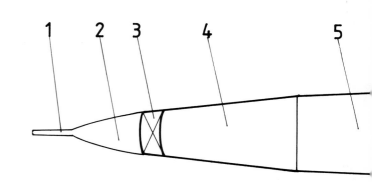

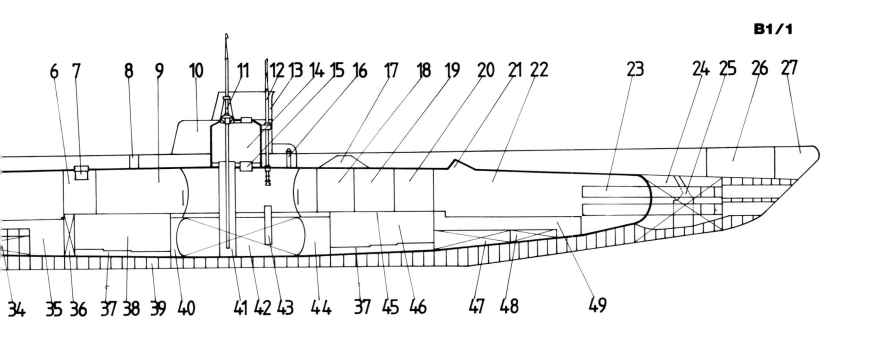

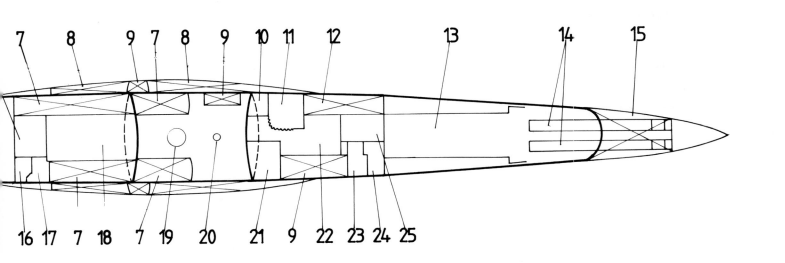

B General arrangements – internal

B2/1 INTERNAL PROFILE, TYPE VIIB

1	Stern casing	29	Forward reserve torpedo container
2	Deck casing knee beam	30	Forward torpedo room and rates' quarters
3	Stern diving tank		
4	Stern (internal) torpedo tube	31	Forward 'subsunk' marker buoy
5	External reserve torpedo container	32	Torpedo tube II
6	Upper deck	33	Watertight bow section
7	Motor room	34	Tow hook housing
8	Stern torpedo loading hatch	35	Bow casing
9	Engine room	36	Starboard rudder
10	Galley	37	Support beam
11	Galley access/escape hatch	38	Free-flooding lower after casing
12	Senior rates' mess and quarters	39	Aft trim tank
13	2cm FlaK pedestal	40	Torpedo compensating tank
14	'Subsunk' marker buoy	41	Lower motor room space
15	Attack centre	42	Engine mountings
16	Attack periscope	43	Battery room I
17	Tower/bridge access/escape hatch (watertight)	44	Fuel oil tank
		45	Main diving tank
18	Control room periscope	46	Magazine
19	Bridge casing	47	*S-Gerät* (sound detection equipment) compartment
20	Main magnetic compass and housing		
		48	Battery room II
21	Control room	49	Torpedo compensating tanks (port and starboard) for tubes I–IV
22	8.8cm main deck gun pedestal		
23	Captain's cabin	50	Forward trim tank
24	Officers' quarters and wardroom	51	Reserve torpedo storage space (4 torpedoes)
25	Watertight ready-use ammunition container (8.8cm ammunition)		
		52	Anchor chain locker (free-flooding)
26	Chief rates' mess and quarters	53	Torpedo tubes forward caps
27	Heads and washroom	54	Strengthened bow plate
28	Forward watertight torpedo loading hatch		

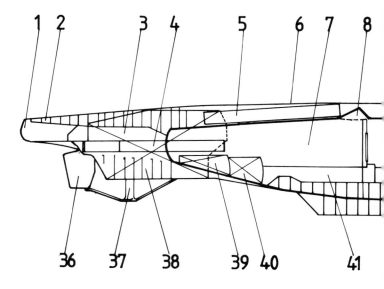

B2/2 INTERNAL PLAN VIEW, TYPE VIIB

1	Aft spacer and aperture for torpedo firing	19	Fresh water tank
		20	Forward automatic battery switching room
2	Aft internal torpedo tube		
3	Torpedo tube support	21	Captain's cabin
4	Stern diving tank	22	Wardroom and officers' quarters
5	Mounting of torpedo tube on pressure hull	23	Chief rates' quarters and mess
		24	Heads and washroom
6	Aft trim tank	25	Forward torpedo compartment and rates' mess
7	Torpedo compensating tanks (port and starboard)		
		26	Torpedo tube II
8	Motor room	27	Aft automatic battery switching room
9	Pressure hull		
10	Engine room	28	Heads
11	Saddle-tank casing	29	Attack periscope sleeve
12	Stringer	30	Control room periscope sleeve
13	Food store	31	Radio room
14	Ballast tank	32	Sound detection room
15	Fuel oil tank	33	Food store
16	Fuel/water compensating tanks	34	Internal bulkhead containing lockers for crew's personal possessions
17	Senior rates' mess and quarters		
18	Air trunk	35	Bow diving tank

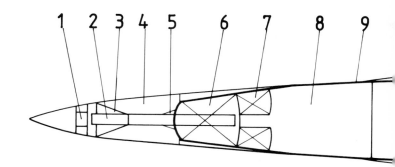

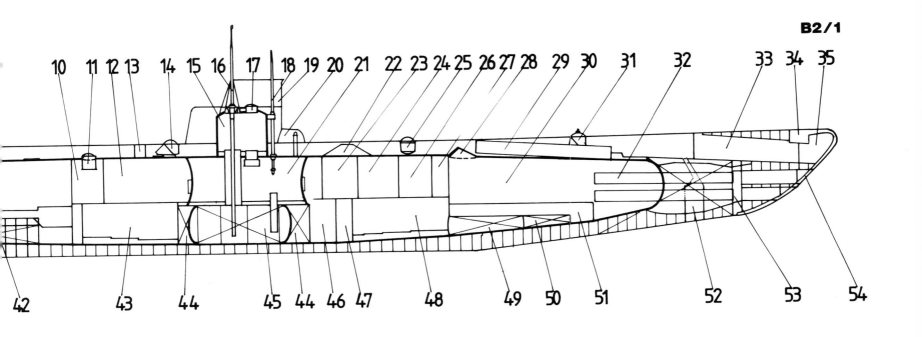

10 11 12 13 14 15 16 17 18 19 20 21 22 23 24 25 26 27 28 29 30 31 32 33 34 35

42 43 44 45 44 46 47 48 49 50 51 52 53 54

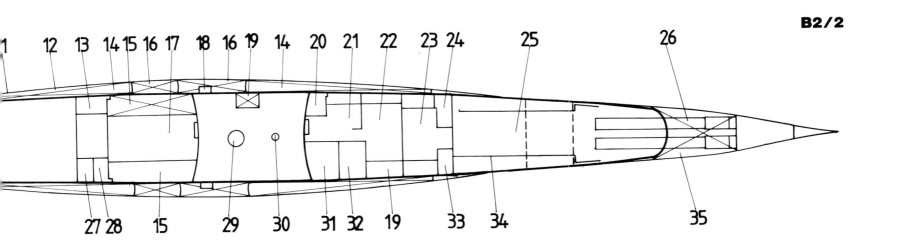

1 12 13 14 15 16 17 18 16 19 14 20 21 22 23 24 25 26

27 28 15 29 30 31 32 19 33 34 35

B General arrangements – internal

B2/3 INTERNAL PLAN OF HOLD, TYPE VIIB
1 Fresh water tank
2 Dirty water tank
3 Battery room I flooring
4 Fuel oil tank
5 Main diving tank
6 Magazine flooring
7 Forward torpedo compensating tanks
8 Forward trim tank

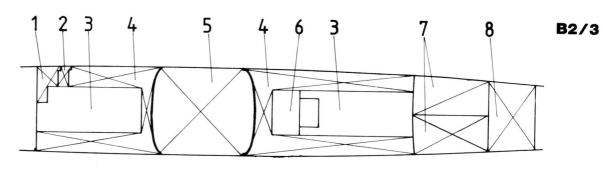

B3/1 INTERNAL PROFILE, TYPE VIIC
1 Stern casing
2 Free-flooding stern
3 Diving tank 1
4 Stern torpedo tube
5 Knee beam (supporting stern casing)
6 Stern torpedo room
7 Reserve torpedo container (watertight)
8 Deck casing
9 Motor room
10 Stern torpedo loading hatch
11 Diesel room
12 Galley
13 Galley access/escape hatch
14 Ready-use ammunition container
15 Lower 'Wintergarten' gun support pedestal
16 Lower 'Wintergarten'
17 Upper 'Wintergarten' ready-use ammunition container
18 Upper 'Wintergarten' gun support pedestal
19 Upper 'Wintergarten'
20 Attack periscope
21 Control room/bridge access/escape hatch
22 Schnorchel tube
23 Schnorchel
24 Schnorchel housing
25 Captain's cabin

26 Officers' wardroom
27 Chief rates' quarters
28 Line of Schnorchel travel
29 Head
30 Forward torpedo loading hatch
31 5 man life raft containers
32 Forward casing support beam
33 Tow hook housing
34 Bow casing
35 Aft trim tank
36 Torpedo compensating tank
37 Reserve torpedo stowage (1 torpedo)
38 Diesel engine mounting
39 Battery room I
40 Main diesel fuel tank I
41 Main diving tank
42 Attack periscope well
43 Control room
44 Main diesel fuel tank
45 Magazines
46 *S-Gerät* compartment
47 Battery room II
48 Torpedo compensating tank
49 Reserve torpedo stowage
50 Forward trim tank
51 Forward torpedo room and crew's quarters
52 Diving tank 5
53 Anchor well
54 Torpedo tube III

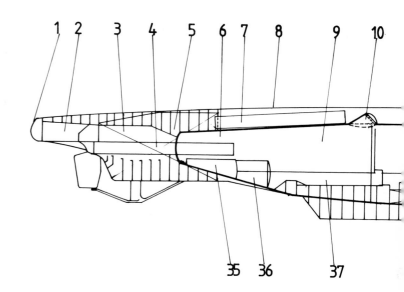

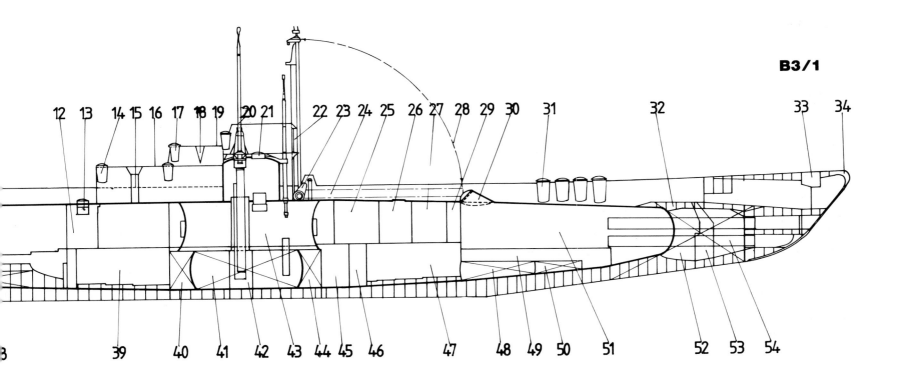

B3/1

12 13 14 15 16 17 18 19 20 21 22 23 24 25 26 27 28 29 30 31 32 33 34

B 39 40 41 42 43 44 45 46 47 48 49 50 51 52 53 54

B General arrangements – internal

B3/2 **INTERNAL PLAN AT WORKING DECK LEVEL, TYPE VIIC**

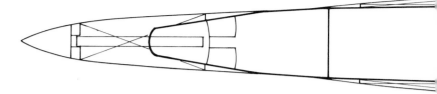

B3/3 **INTERNAL PLAN OF HOLD, TYPE VIIC**

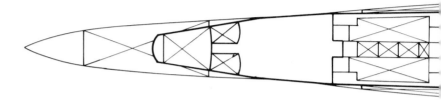

B4/1 **INTERNAL PROFILE, TYPE VIID** (with the exception of the inserted section between Frames 39 and 40 the internal details are as for the VIIC. Frames within the extension, as in Drawing B5/1, were lettered A to N)

1 Upper mine shaft closing grating
2 Mine shaft number IV (numbered from forward)
3 Casing, mine shaft housing
4 Fuel oil tank
5 Frame 39
6 Lubricating oil tank (starboard) fresh water tank (port)
7 Mine shaft lower reinforcing ring (shafts were free-flooding)
8 Frame 40

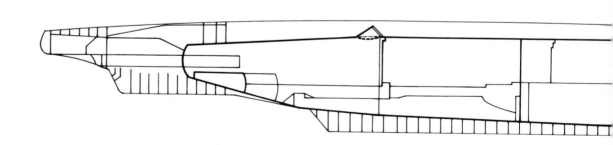

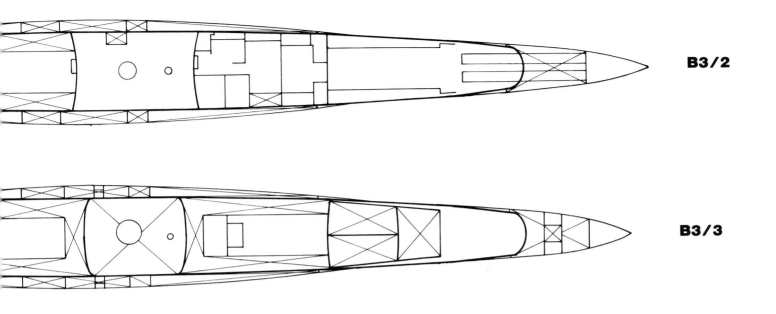

B3/2

B3/3

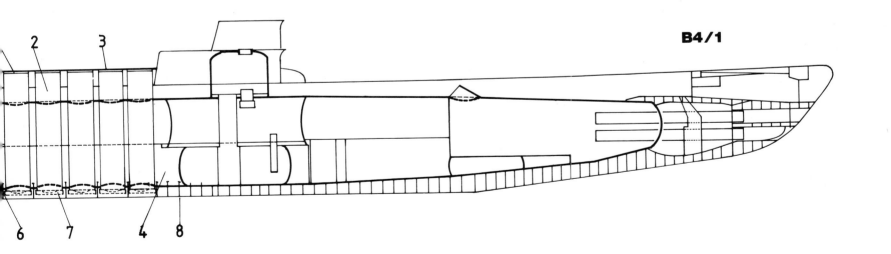

B4/1

2   3

6   7   4   8

B General arrangements – internal

B4/2 INTERNAL PLAN, PRESSURE HULL DECK LEVEL, TYPE VIID
1 Engine room
2 Fuel oil tank
3 Senior rates' mess
4 Mine compensating tank (6 in all)
5 Ballast tank (water-filled)
6 Ballast tank (initially filled with fuel oil and free-filling with sea water as fuel content diminished)
7 Fuel oil tank
8 Mine compensating tanks (4 in all)
9 Negative buoyancy tank
10 Fuel oil tank
11 Accommodation space
12 Mine release gear
13 Mine shaft I
14 Head
15 Control room
16 Officers' and chief rates' quarters

B4/3 INTERNAL PLAN AT LEVEL OF KEEL PLATING, TYPE VIID
1 Fresh water tank
2 Lubricating oil tank
3 Fuel oil tank
4 Mine shaft IV
5 Mine compensating tanks

B5/1 INTERNAL PROFILE, TYPE VIIF (the note to Drawing B4/1 also applies to this drawing)
1 Galley
2 Senior rates' mess
3 Midships torpedo loading hatch
4 Torpedo stowage
5 Reserve torpedo container (port and starboard)
6 Potato store
7 Senior rates' number II mess
8 Heads
9 Fuel oil tank
10 Battery room I
11 Frame 39
12 Torpedo compensating tanks
13 Lubricating oil tank
14 Dirty water tank
15 Frame 40

B5/2 PLAN OF HOLD AT PRESSURE HULL DECK LEVEL, TYPE VIIF
1 Fuel oil tank
2 Food store
3 Refrigerator
4 Fuel oil tank
5 Senior rates' mess
6 Ballast tank (initially fuel, with sea water replacing used fuel)
7 Torpedo compensating tanks (fuel with sea water replacement)
8 Refrigerator II
9 Heads
10 Negative buoyancy tank (port and starboard)
11 Engine room
12 Galley
13 Walkway in torpedo storage compartment
14 Main torpedo storage compartment
15 Potato store access hatch
16 Senior rates' number II mess
17 Control room
18 Officers' quarters and chief rates' mess

B4/2

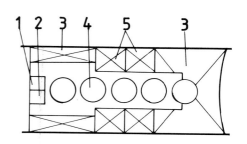

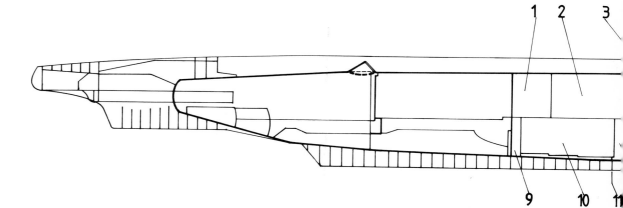

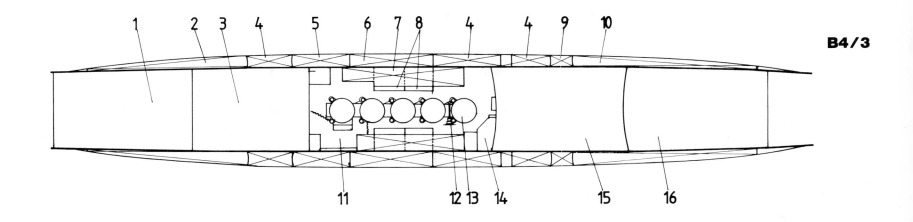

B4/3

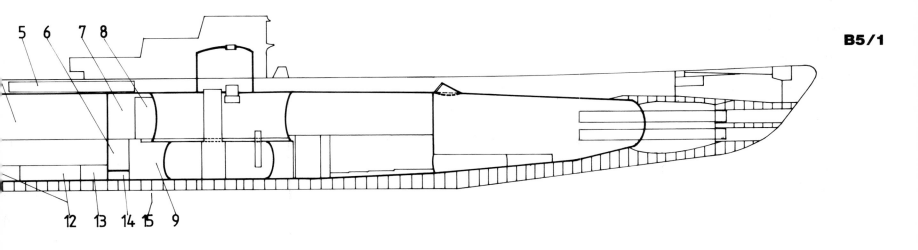

B5/1

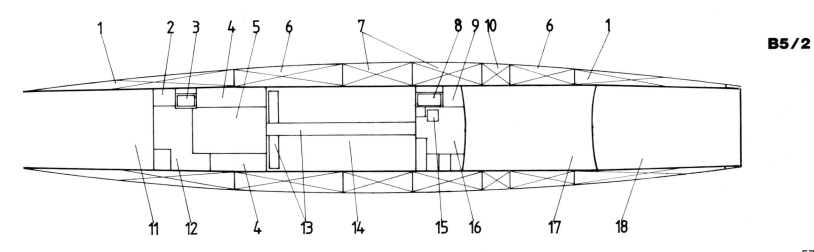

B5/2

57

B General arrangements – internal

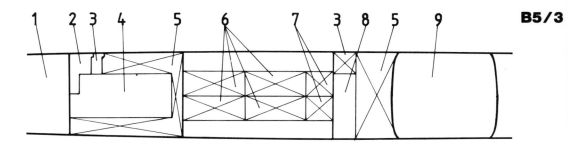

B5/3

B6

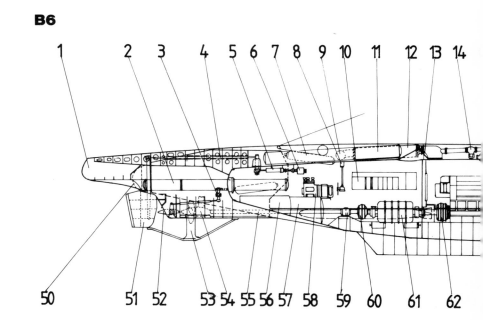

B6 LONGITUDINAL SECTION, TYPE VIIB

1 Stern casing
2 Stringer III
3 Stringer IV
4 Rudder control shaft
5 Rudder control master cylinder
6 Rudder control gear
7 High pressure air bottle
8 Rudder control wheel
9 Diesel surface exhaust
10 Electrical control panel
11 Deck reserve torpedo container
12 Diesel exhaust silencer
13 Aft torpedo loading hatch
14 Diesel exhaust output exchange valve
15 High pressure air bottle
16 Galley
17 Galley escape/access hatch
18 Diesel air inlet trunking
19 Aft quarters (senior rates)
20 'Subsunk' marker buoy (released from inside the boat)
21 Washroom and heads
22 Diesel surface air inlet mast
23 Boat air inlet mast (trunking not shown)
24 Attack periscope sleeve
25 Attack periscope
26 Bridge access/escape hatch
27 Control room and air search periscope
28 Control room
29 Main magnetic compass
30 Internal bulkhead door
31 Mounting for forward deck gun
32 Watertight ready-use locker (for 8.8cm ammunition)
33 Forward torpedo loading hatch
34 Locker (one of 18)
35 Bunk (one of 6)
36 Forward torpedo room and ratings' quarters
37 Forward deck reserve torpedo casing
38 Forward 'subsunk' marker buoy
39 Controls for windlass/capstan
40 Capstan head
41 Motor control for windlass/capstan (forward or backward motion control)
42 Spring-loaded pulley for aerial tension control
43 Drive arm for anchor winch
44 Anchor windlass
45 Anchor housing (starboard only)
46 High pressure air bottle
47 Bow support beam
48 Deck 'A' of bow
49 Bow casing
50 Stern torpedo tube opening
51 Port rudder (one of two)
52 Stern hydroplane (one of two)
53 Rudder support post (centreline)
54 Propeller boss (one of two)
55 Propeller shaft (one of two)
56 Stern trim tank
57 Torpedo compensating tank (port and starboard)
58 Auxiliary generator
59 Propeller shaft bearing
60 Gear box
61 Main electric motor (two)
62 Engine gear box and clutch
63 Main diesel engine (two)
64 Engine room
65 Engine oil sump
66 Aft battery room
67 Main diving tank pump
68 Master gyro compass
69 Keel
70 Attack periscope sleeve
71 Attack periscope well (dry)
72 Main diving tank inlet valve (two)
73 Oil fuel tank Ii
74 Radio stores locker
75 Magazine
76 Forward battery room
77 Cells of battery room II
78 Torpedo compensating tank 2
79 Reserve torpedo stowage
80 Forward trim tank
81 Torpedo tube III
82 Forward hydroplane attitude control motor
83 Windlass and capstan motor
84 Control transmission arm for forward hydroplanes
85 Forward hydroplane (two)
86 Outer section of torpedo tube III
87 Torpedo tube bow door
88 Bow casing deck 'A'
89 Bow casing deck 'C'

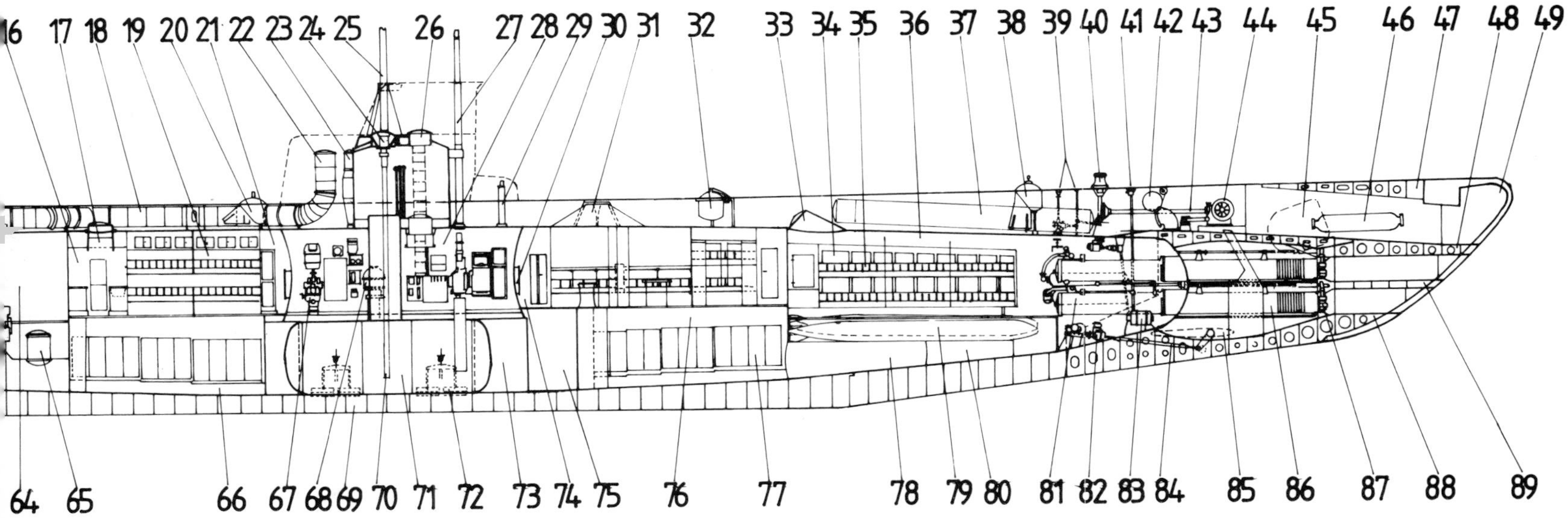

B General arrangements – internal

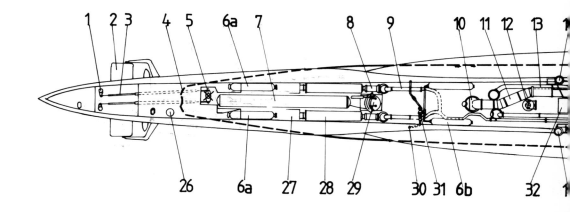

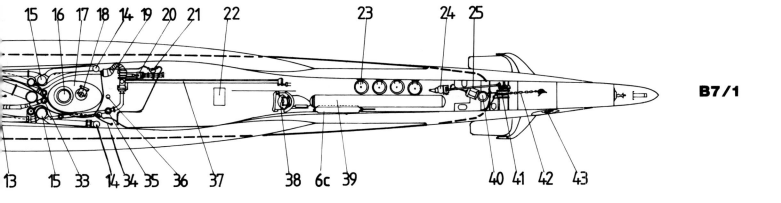

15 16 17 18 14 19 20 21 22   23   24 25

B7/1

13 15 33 14 34 35 36 37   38 6c 39   40 41 42 43

B General arrangements – internal

B7/2 INTERNAL WORKING DECK PLAN, TYPE VIIC

1 Stringer
2 Stringer
3 Stringer
4 High pressure air supply for torpedo tube V
5 Auxiliary generator
6 Main reduction gearing and clutch
7 Main electric motor
8 High pressure oxygen bottles
9 High pressure air for starting diesel engines
10 Diesel engine
11 Oil cooler
12 High pressure air group 3
13 Main diving tank voiding pump
14 Deck plating
15 Control room periscope sleeve
16 Control room periscope drive motor
17 Access hatch to magazine
18 Captain's quarters
19 Access to *S-Gerät* space
20 Officers' mess
21 Lockers
22 Heads and washroom
23 Bunks
24 High pressure air supply for port torpedo tubes
25 Torpedo tube
26 Bow casing deck 'D'
27 Stern torpedo tube door
28 Stern hydroplane control arm
29 Stern hydroplane control motor
30 Stern torpedo tube
31 Stern hydroplane hydraulic servo motor
32 Oxygen bottles
33 Junkers air compressor
34 Motor room deck support pedestal
35 Drive shaft
36 Engine room deck
37 Starboard saddle tank
38 Engineers' mess
39 Main control station for all diving and trim tanks
40 Oxygen bottles
41 Attack periscope trunking and sleeve
42 Aft hydroplane control station (hydraulic/manual)
43 Forward hydroplane control station
44 Radio room
45 Sound room
46 Drinking water tank 3
47 Chief rates' quarters
48 Lockers
49 Food store
50 Forward torpedo room and ratings' quarters
51 Leaf table
52 Non-slip deck
53 Torpedo tube III

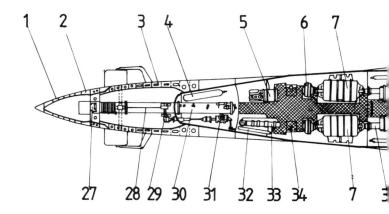

B7/3 INTERNAL PLAN AT LEVEL OF HOLD, TYPE VIIC

1 Stringer III
2 Hydroplane drive motor
3 Stringer II
4 Stern trim tank
5 Torpedo compensating tank
6 Electric motor mounting
7 Motor room bilge
8 Reserve torpedo
9 Clean water tank
10 Foul water tank
11 Foul water tank
12 Reserve torpedo storage
13 Reserve torpedoes–not fitted with pistols
14 Forward hydroplane
15 Anchor chain well
16 Bow casing
17 Starboard rudder
18 Clutch pedestal (electric motor)
19 Main bilge supports, diesel engines
20 Diesel room bilge
21 Attack periscope well
22 Main diving tank
23 Washing water tank
24 Battery room II
25 Support beam, forward torpedo storage space
26 Forward hydroplane drive motor
27 Bow cap of pressure hull
28 Forward hydroplane arm cap
29 Forward hydroplane arm

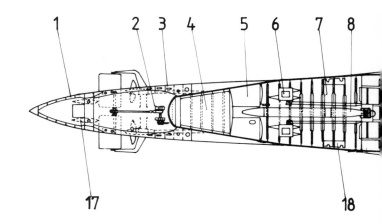

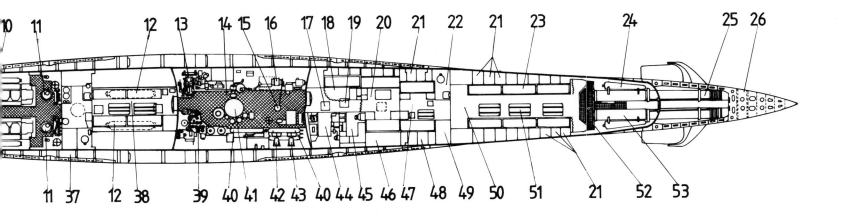

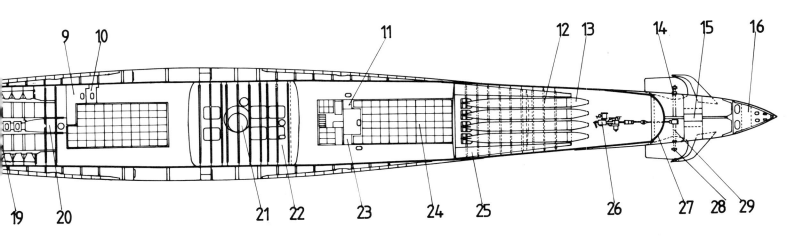

B General arrangements – internal

B7/4 AIR SUPPLY AND EXHAUST TRUNKING FOR BOATS FITTED WITH SCHNORCHEL, TYPE VIIC (1/100 scale)

1 Diesel exhaust outlets
2 Diesel exhaust silencer boxes
3 Exhaust outlet control valves and pressure casing apertures
4 Schnorchel exhaust pipes
5 Single exhaust to Schnorchel
6 Engine air inlet (surface or Schnorchal run)
7 Air inlets to engine room (surface running only)
8 Main air inlet trunking
9 Main surface air inlet (note Schnorchel connection immediately aft)
10 Air inlet masts (surface running)
11 Schnorchel trunking (extra to standard fittings)
12 Conning tower outline
13 Schnorchel air inlet connection, operating only when Schnorchel mast raised
14 Diesel exhaust to Schnorchel (operating only when Schnorchel mast raised)

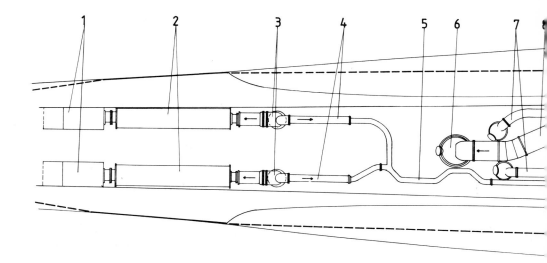

B7/5 LONGITUDINAL SECTION, TYPE VIIC/41

This general section of a VIIC/41 shows the internal arrangement of the boats. The greater sophistication of the tower is the most obvious point, as well as the increased provision fo escape rafts (forward, and in the lower *'Wintergarten'* position). The drawings of the individual compartments in Section D are annotated to give full details.

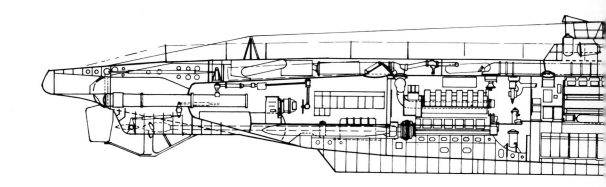

B7/4

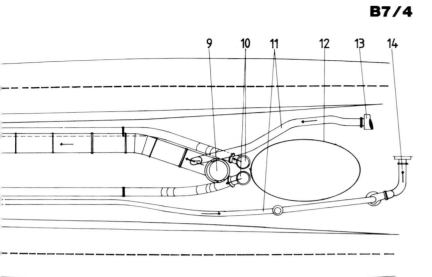

9   10   11   12   13   14

B7/5

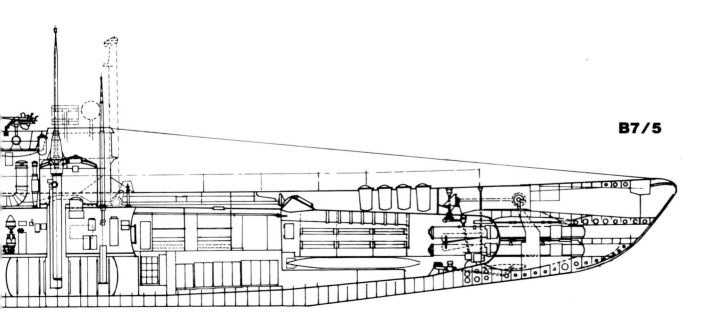

B General arrangements – internal

B7/6 **PLATING THICKNESSES (IRON PLAN), TYPE VIIC/41 (elevation and lower deck plan)**
The boat is shown in longitudinal section with plate thicknesses in millimetres. The contents of each section are shown in the more detailed plans, as are the fittings of the lower deck plan.

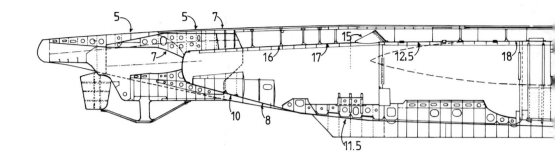

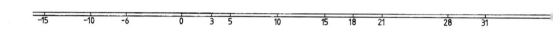

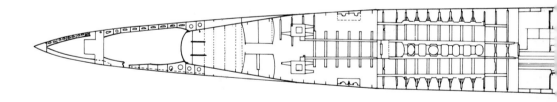

B7/7 **TYPE VIIC MAIN AIR INLET MASTS AND TRUNKING (aft part of conning tower; no scale)**
1 Connector to boat air supply (starboard only)
2 Line of bridge casing
3 Air inlet heads
4 Schnorchel connector pipe
5 Boat air supply junction
6 Diesel room air supply control valve
7 Diesel room air inlets
8 Boat air supply connector slide control
9 Forward inlet pipe to Schnorchel
10 Protective cap and gland
11 Motor room control valve
12 Pressure hull
13 Outer casing
14 Air inlet masts

B7/7

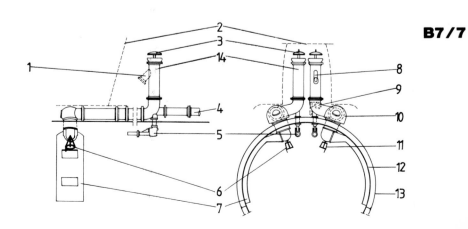

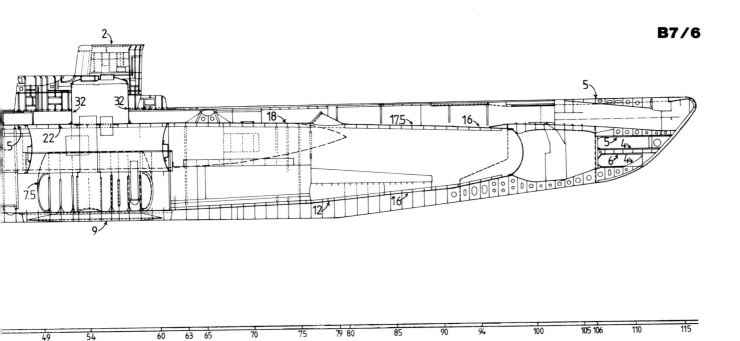

B7/6

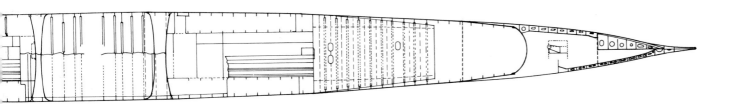

C Hull sections

C1-11   **TYPE VIIC HULL SECTIONS (all to 1/100 scale)**

C1

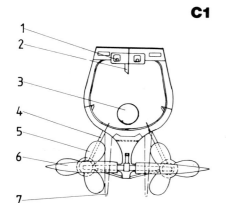

C2

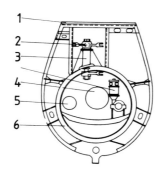

C3

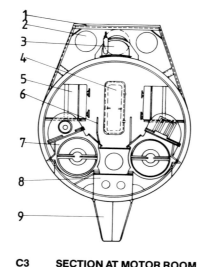

C4

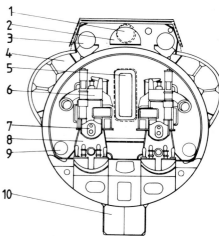

C1	**SECTION AT STERN HYDROPLANE MOUNTING**
1	Rudder control arm
2	Knee beam
3	Stern torpedo tube (number V)
4	Support bracket for propeller shaft
5	Propeller blade
6	Hydroplane
7	Line of rudder (aft of section point)

C2	**SECTION AT STERN OF AFT TORPEDO ROOM**
1	Casing deck
2	Rudder control arm head
3	Mounting for rudder arm head
4	Torpedo tube V
5	High pressure air bottle
6	Pressure hull

C3	**SECTION AT MOTOR ROOM**
1	Casing deck
2	Diesel exhaust
3	Aft torpedo loading hatch
4	Access door to stern room
5	Starboard electrical control board
6	Safety railing
7	Starboard electric motor
8	Support housing
9	Keel

C4	**SECTION AT DIESEL COMPARTMENT**
1	Reserve torpedo container
2	Diesel exhaust
3	Diesel air inlet trunking
4	Starboard saddle-tank
5	Access door to motor room
6	Starboard diesel engine
7	Starter motor
8	Engine mounting
9	High pressure air cylinder for engine starter
10	Keel

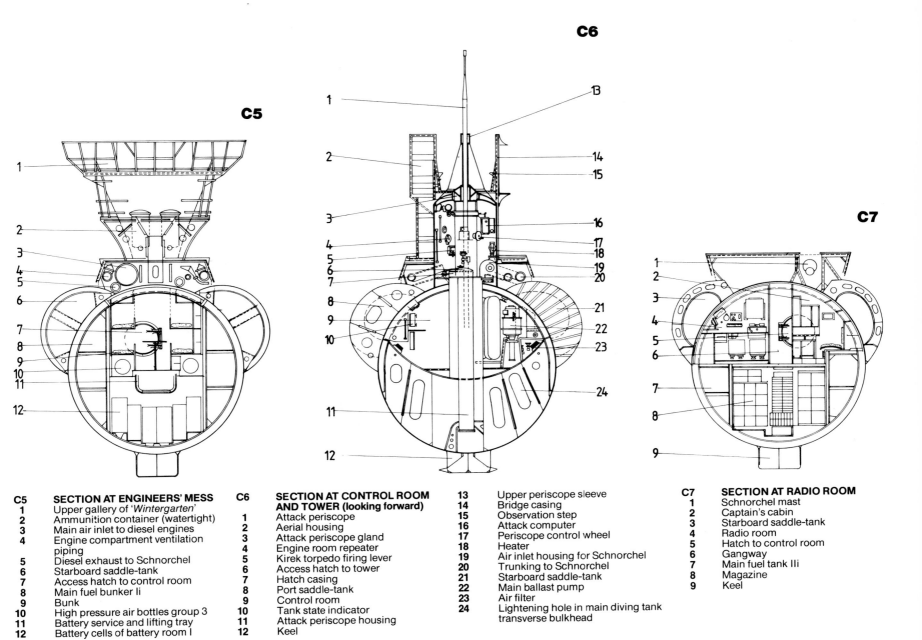

C5

C6

C7

C5	SECTION AT ENGINEERS' MESS
1	Upper gallery of 'Wintergarten'
2	Ammunition container (watertight)
3	Main air inlet to diesel engines
4	Engine compartment ventilation piping
5	Diesel exhaust to Schnorchel
6	Starboard saddle-tank
7	Access hatch to control room
8	Main fuel bunker Ii
9	Bunk
10	High pressure air bottles group 3
11	Battery service and lifting tray
12	Battery cells of battery room I

C6	SECTION AT CONTROL ROOM AND TOWER (looking forward)
1	Attack periscope
2	Aerial housing
3	Attack periscope gland
4	Engine room repeater
5	Kirek torpedo firing lever
6	Access hatch to tower
7	Hatch casing
8	Port saddle-tank
9	Control room
10	Tank state indicator
11	Attack periscope housing
12	Keel

13	Upper periscope sleeve
14	Bridge casing
15	Observation step
16	Attack computer
17	Periscope control wheel
18	Heater
19	Air inlet housing for Schnorchel
20	Trunking to Schnorchel
21	Starboard saddle-tank
22	Main ballast pump
23	Air filter
24	Lightening hole in main diving tank transverse bulkhead

C7	SECTION AT RADIO ROOM
1	Schnorchel mast
2	Captain's cabin
3	Starboard saddle-tank
4	Radio room
5	Hatch to control room
6	Gangway
7	Main fuel tank IIi
8	Magazine
9	Keel

C Hull sections

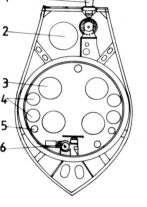

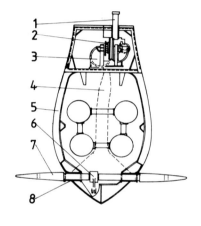

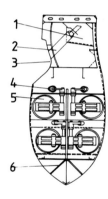

C8	SECTION AT FORWARD TORPEDO ROOM
1	Reserve torpedo container
2	Forward torpedo loading hatch
3	Access door to officers' and senior ratings' quarters
4	Forward torpedo room mess
5	High pressure air bottles group 5
6	Reserve torpedo stowage locations
7	Torpedo compensating tank
8	Bilge casing
9	Keel

C9	SECTION AT CAPSTAN
1	Capstan
2	Forward reserve torpedo container
3	Torpedo tube I
4	High pressure air bottles for torpedo tubes I and III
5	High pressure airline
6	Forward hydroplane control motor

C10	SECTION AT FORWARD HYDROPLANES
1	Bollard
2	Anchor windlass
3	Forward torpedo container
4	Main stem post
5	Outer casing
6	Hydroplane link
7	Starboard hydroplane blade
8	Hydroplane gland and seal

C11	SECTION AT BOW TORPEDO TUBE DOORS
1	Deck stores stowage space
2	Anchor sleeve
3	Outer casing
4	Control arm for torpedo tube I door
5	Door to torpedo tube I
6	Bow fairing plate

D Compartments

D   **COMPARTMENTS, TYPE VIIC**
(unless otherwise noted, all
drawings in this section are to 1/100
scale)

D1/1   **STERN, INTERNAL PROFILE**
(showing steering controls)

1	Stern casing
2	Stringer III
3	Rudder post
4	Rudder post universal joint
5	Rudder linkage
6	Bollards
7	Upper casing of diving tank 1
8	Aerial/jumping wire
9	Stern navigation light
10	Rudder control linkage
11	Rudder control motor
12	Fixed deck rails
13	Rudder transmission arm
14	Emergency wheel
15	Gear box
16	Reserve torpedo container
17	Stern torpedo outlet
18	Rudder
19	Stern torpedo tube support arm
20	Hydroplane
21	Stern torpedo tube
22	Propeller boss
23	Hydroplane control arm
24	Hydroplane control linkage
25	Hydroplane control arm
26	Hydroplane control piston
27	Hydroplane control motor
28	Stern trim tank
29	Propeller shaft
30	Torpedo compensating tank
31	Deck
32	Stern torpedo room and motor room

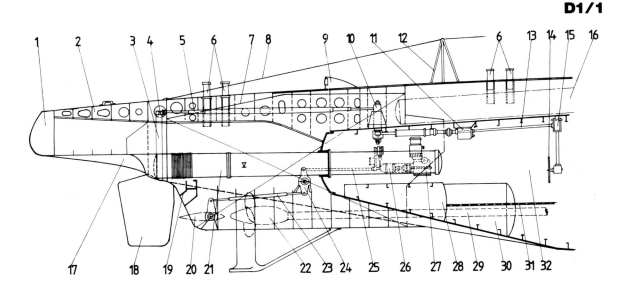

D1/1

D Compartments

D1/2 STERN, PLAN BELOW OUTER CASING LEVEL

1 Stern casing
2 Outlet valve for diving tank 1
3 Support plate for stern casing
4 Port rudder
5 Port rudder post
6 Port hydroplane
7 Port propeller
8 Port hydroplane fairing
9 Outlet valve for diving tank 1 (below)
10 Rudder control arm
11 Inlet valve for diving tank 1 (below)
12 Pressure hull line
13 Rudder control housing and gland
14 Rudder control access space
15 Forward point of stern casing
16 Reserve torpedo container (watertight)

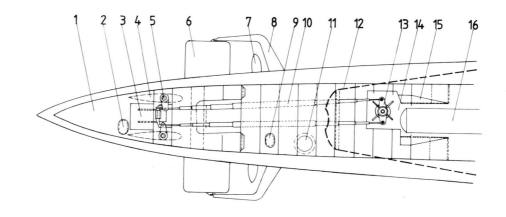

D1/2

D1/3 STERN, PLAN AT WORKING DECK LEVEL

1 Stringer III
2 Free-flooding stern
3 Port rudder
4 Port rudder post
5 Stern torpedo door hinge
6 Port hydroplane
7 Port hydroplane fairing
8 Port propeller
9 Port propeller hub
10 Hydroplane control linkage
11 Stern torpedo tube
12 Hydroplane control gears
13 Stringer II
14 High pressure air bottle
15 Hydroplane control piston
16 Hydroplane control arm
17 Hydroplane control motor
18 Hydroplane control linkage to control room (hydraulic/manual)
19 Forward line of stern trim tank

D1/3

D1/4 STERN, PLAN AT HYDROPLANE LEVEL

1 Stringer III
2 Free-flooding stern
3 Port rudder
4 Rudder beam
5 Port hydroplane
6 Port hydroplane arm
7 Horizontal support beam
8 Stringer II
9 Hydroplane attitude control motor
10 Support beam of stern trim tank
11 Stern trim tank
12 Torpedo compensating tanks
13 Diving tank 1
14 Hydroplane attitude drive arm
15 Hydroplane motor linkage
16 Pressure hull

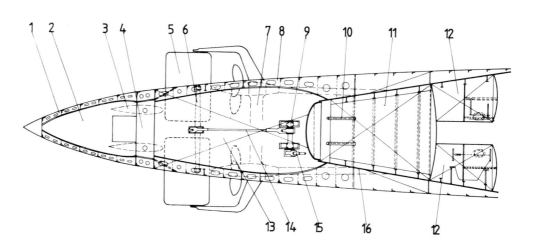

D1/4

D1/5 **STERN GENERAL ARRANGEMENTS, TYPE VIIC/41** (similar to the early design, but with more effective arrangement of the hydroplanes, rudders and the propeller housings)

1 Stern casing
2 Stern casing drainage slots
3 Stern torpedo tube outer door (closed)
4 Starboard rudder
5 Starboard rudder post
6 Starboard rudder post gland and seal
7 Starboard rudder support arm
8 Starboard aft hydroplane
9 Keel casing drainage slots
10 Stern post
11 Propeller blade (3-bladed propellers port and starboard)
12 Propeller hub
13 Hydroplane support extension arm
14 Propeller housing
15 Propeller housing support arm
16 Line of stern outer casing
17 Propeller shaft
18 Keel casing drainage slots
19 Propeller watertight housing and gland

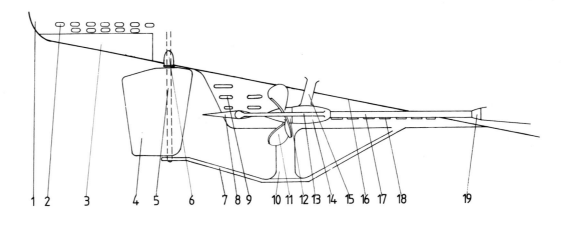

D1/6 **GENERAL VIEW OF PROPELLERS AND RUDDERS COMMON TO ALL TYPE VII BOATS (no scale)**

1 Propeller shaft housing and watertight gland
2 Propeller shaft
3 Aft casing
4 Keel casing extension
5 Hydroplane support extension arm
6 Propeller housing
7 Propeller blade (3-bladed propeller)
8 Propeller hub
9 Stern post
10 Port hydroplane
11 Rudder supports
12 Port rudder control extension arm
13 Port rudder
14 Starboard rudder

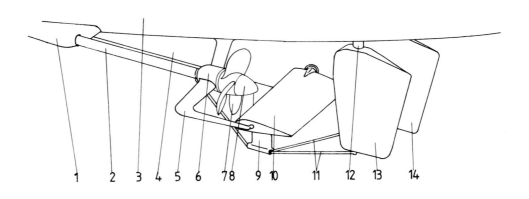

D Compartments

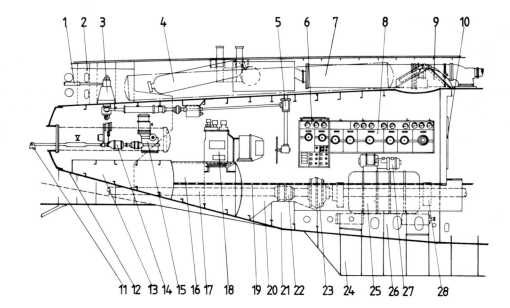

D2/1

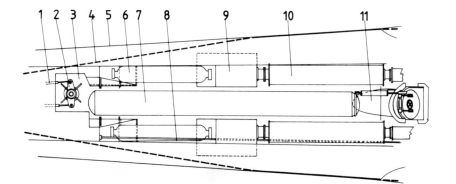

D2/2

D2/3 MOTOR ROOM AND STERN TORPEDO ROOM, PLAN AT DECK LEVEL

1 Stringer II
2 High pressure air supply for stern torpedo tube
3 Stern torpedo tube (number V)
4 Pressure hull
5 Outer casing
6 Stern torpedo compensating tank (port and starboard)
7 Auxiliary generator
8 Oiling gland for propeller shaft
9 Clutch
10 Main electric motor
11 Drive shaft
12 Stern hydroplane control arm
13 Stern trim tank
14 Stern hydroplane hydraulic servo motor
15 Junkers air compressor feed hose to high pressure air reservoir
16 Junkers air compressor
17 Non-slip deck
18 Motor support mounting
19 Bulkhead door to engine room

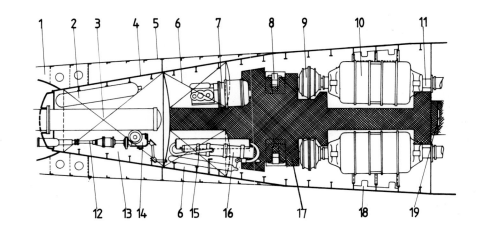

D2/4 MOTOR ROOM AND STERN TORPEDO ROOM, PLAN AT HOLD LEVEL

1 Pressure hull stern cap
2 Stringer II
3 Support beam
4 Aft diving tank
5 Bulkhead for diving tank
6 Torpedo compensating tank (port and starboard)
7 Reserve torpedo (one)
8 Deck support mountings
9 Motor support mounting
10 Motor/engine room bulkhead

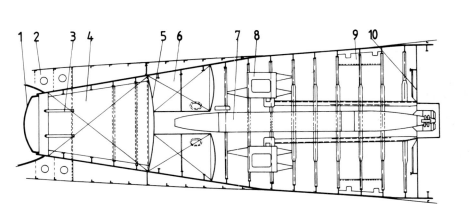

D Compartments

D3/1 ENGINE ROOM, INTERNAL PROFILE (showing exhaust system)

1. Diesel exhaust box
2. Diesel exhaust silencer
3. Motor room
4. Deck casing
5. Aft torpedo loading hatch
6. Diesel room/motor room connecting door
7. Diesel exhaust coupling
8. Electric control panel
9. Forward diesel exhaust (leading to Schnorchel)
10. Port diesel engine
11. Cooling water header tank
12. High pressure air bottle
13. Air inlet to diesel room (from normal air trunking abaft the bridge and from Schnorchel)
14. Air inlet control valve
15. Air inlet bleeder valve
16. Air inlet trunking
17. Propeller shaft
18. Clutch
19. Pressure hull
20. Engine mounting
21. Deck
22. Diesel air pressure starter
23. Fuel oil cooler/filter
24. Fuel oil feed
25. Bulkhead
26. Bulkhead door

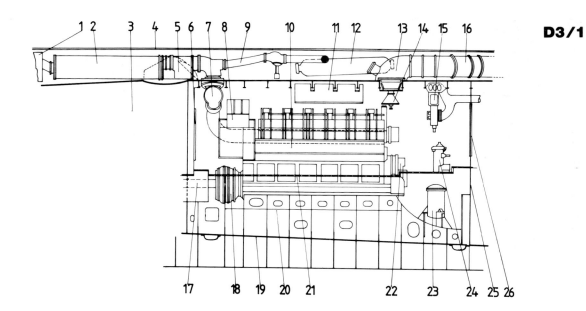

D3/2 ENGINE ROOM, PLAN AT WORKING DECK

1. Starboard propeller shaft housing
2. Pressure hull
3. Outer casing of saddle-tank
4. High pressure oxygen bottle
5. Diesel cylinder head and fuel injector assembly
6. High pressure air supply to starboard diesel engine starter
7. Saddle-tank diving tank 2 (port and starboard)
8. Oil fuel pump
9. Slave oil fuel pump controls and valves for starboard engine
10. Rear engine housing and clutch
11. Exhaust
12. Port saddle-tank (and see 7)
13. Engine starter (compressed air operated)
14. Oil cooler
15. Main oil fuel inlet control valve
16. Master oil fuel control valves

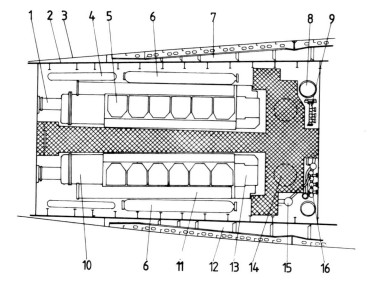

D4/1 **ENGINEERS' AND SENIOR RATES' MESS, LONGITUDINAL SECTION**

1 Hatch to diesel engine room
2 Galley
3 Galley escape hatch
4 Main diesel air inlet trunking
5 Engineers' and senior rates' mess
6 Bunk
7 Pressure hull
8 Locker
9 Outer casing (line of)
10 Wardrobe
11 Aft bulkhead of control room
12 Pressure-tight hatch
13 Bulkhead
14 Food store
15 Sink
16 High pressure air group
17 Shock-proof flooring
18 Keel
19 Battery room I
20 Main fuel bunker Ii

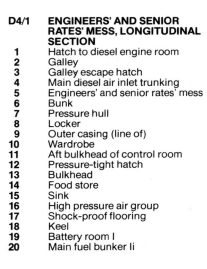
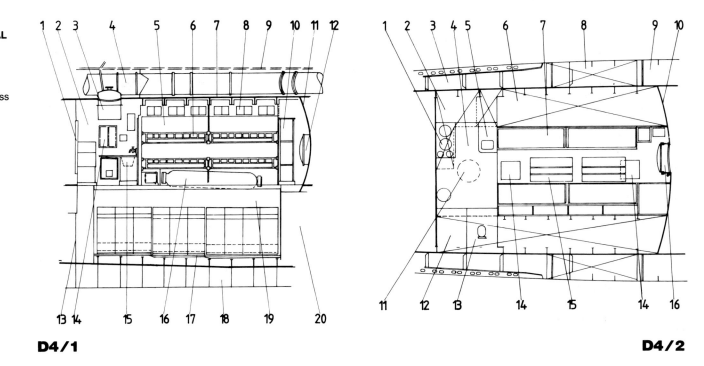

D4/1

D4/2

D4/3

D4/2 **ENGINEERS' AND SENIOR RATES' MESS, PLAN AT WORKING DECK LEVEL**

1 Stove
2 Food stores
3 Saddle-tank diving tank 2
4 Galley
5 Sink
6 Fuel oil bunker Ii
7 Bunks (2 x 1)
8 Regulating tank 1
9 Regulating tank 2
10 Forward bulkhead
11 Escape/access hatch outline
12 Battery switching room I
13 Heads
14 Access hatches to battery compartment (below)
15 Folding mess tables
16 Watertight hatch through bulkhead

D4/3 **ENGINEERS' AND SENIOR RATES' MESS, PLAN BELOW WORKING DECK LEVEL (battery room I)**

1 Bulkhead between battery room I and engine room bilge
2 Ballast tank 2 (port and starboard)
3 Vent for fresh water tank
4 Fresh water tank 1
5 Dirty water collection tank 1
6 Main oil fuel tank Ii
7 Regulating tank 1 (port and starboard)
8 Regulating tank 2 (port and starboard)
9 Pressure bulkhead of main diving tank
10 Engine room bilge
11 Battery cells of battery room I
12 Main diving tank

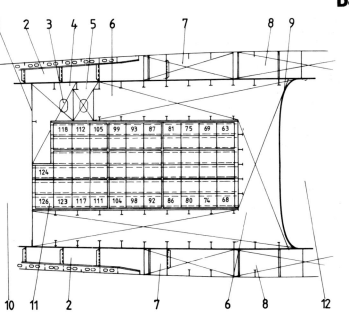

77

D Compartments

D5/1 **CONTROL ROOM AND TOWER,**
LONGITUDINAL SECTION

1. Diesel air inlet mast (surface running)
2. Boat air inlet mast (surface running)
3. Collision reinforcement
4. Attack periscope outer housing
5. Attack periscope stem
6. Tower access/escape hatch
7. Control room/air search periscope
8. Pressure hull
9. Torpedo firing order instruments
10. Main diving tank pump
11. Fuse box
12. Watertight hatch in aft bulkhead (leading to engineers' quarters)
13. Auxiliary pump controls
14. By-pass valve for main diving tank
15. Main oil fuel tank Ii
16. Main diving tank frame
17. Keel
18. Kirek torpedo firing lever
19. Nightsight heater
20. Revolution repeater (propeller shaft speed)
21. Compass repeater
22. Torpedo director
23. Casing outline
24. Access hatch to tower
25. Control room periscope gland
26. Firing system switches
27. Firing system fuses
28. Automatic salvo switch
29. Forward watertight hatch (leading to forward part of boat)
30. Main fuse box
31. Air search periscope well
32. Main oil fuel tank Iii
33. Main diving tank

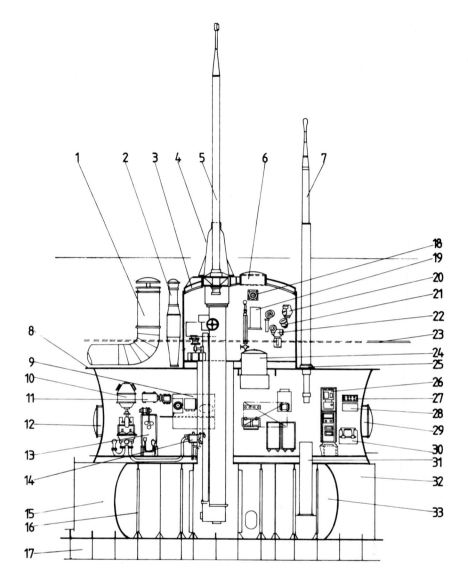

OFFICERS' AND SENIOR RATES' QUARTERS, INTERNAL PROFILE

1. Access hatch through forward main bulkhead
2. Forward main bulkhead
3. Air pipe
4. Battery self-regulating room access door
5. Bunks
6. Lockers and shelves
7. Schnorchel mast (stowed)
8. Outer casing deck
9. Locker
10. Battery loading hatch
11. Wardrobe
12. Senior ratings' bunks
13. Access door to forward heads
14. Schnorchel head
15. Battery ventilation pipe
16. Main fuel tank IIi
17. Magazine pallet
18. Ammunition boxes
19. Washing water tank
20. Forward battery room
21. Individual battery cells
22. Battery room cushioned flooring
23. Keel
24. Forward torpedo room
25. Hold of forward torpedo room

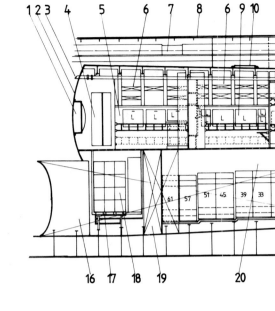

D6/2 OFFICERS' AND SENIOR RATES' QUARTERS, PLAN OF PRESSURE HULL ABOVE

(showing the general arrangement of the Schnorchel piping and the battery loading hatch; this was sealed. The high pressure air hoses are also to be seen)

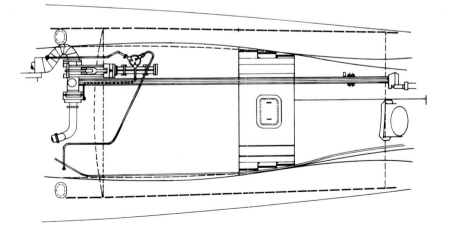

D Compartments

D6/3   **OFFICERS' AND SENIOR RATES' QUARTERS, PLAN AT DECK LEVEL**

1	Pressure-tight bulkhead door to control room
2	Saddle-tank, diving tank 4
3	Saddle-tank stringer
4	Battery self-regulating room 2
5	Access hatch to battery space (below)
6	Captain's bunk
7	Locker ('L' being common)
8	Air-tight locker for confidential books
9	Access hatch to magazine
10	Mess table
11	Bunks (2)
12	Heads
13	Forward torpedo room
14	Bulkhead
15	Radio room
16	Sound location room
17	Ballast tank 4
18	Fresh water tank 2
19	Chief rates' mess
20	Mess table (folding)
21	Food store
22	Bulkhead
23	Acces hatch to forward torpedo room

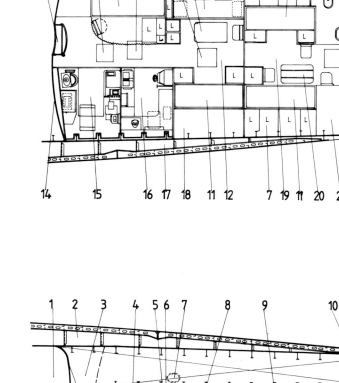

D6/4   **OFFICERS' AND CHIEF RATES' QUARTERS, PLAN BELOW DECK LEVEL (battery room II)**

1	Main diving tank
2	Ballast tank 4
3	Main fuel tank IIi
4	Magazine
5	*S-Gerät* room
6	Dirty water tank 2
7	Water inlet valve
8	Bilge access
9	Battery cells of forward battery room
10	Cell number 1–cells were numbered port to starboard, from forward aft
11	Forward bulkhead
12	Diving tank 4
13	Washing water tank
14	Access to bilge
15	Water inlet valve
16	Starboard section of main fuel tank IIi
17	Hold of forward torpedo room

D6/5 **GENERAL VIEW OF CAPTAIN'S QUARTERS (looking forward; no scale)**
1   Captain's bunk/seat
2   Curtain
3   Reading light
4   Main light
5   Radio/intercom and course repeater
6   Hatch to forward torpedo room
7   Light
8   Air trunking
9   Captain's table
10   Chair
11   Wardroom bunks
12   Forward torpedo tube loading hatch ladder

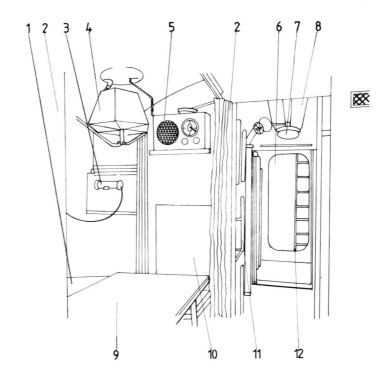

D7/1 **BOW TORPEDO ROOM AND CREW'S QUARTERS, INTERNAL PROFILE**
1   Air supply piping
2   Forward torpedo loading hatch cover
3   Easing spring for torpedo loading hatch cover
4   Forward bollards (removable at sea)
5   Forward reserve torpedo watertight container (1 torpedo)
6   High pressure air group 6
7   Crew's bunks
8   Watertight container for 5 man inflatable life raft (four such)
9   Release handle for lid
10   Personal locker
11   Control linkage for windlass/capstan
12   Deck control point for windlass/capstan
13   Capstan head
14   Gear mounting for windlass/capstan
15   Transmission arm to windlass
16   Universal joint on power transmission
17   Motor control
18   Anchor windlass
19   Reinforced support plating for windlass
20   Forward collision bulkhead
21   Watertight locker
22   Torpedo compensating tank 2
23   Forward trim tank
24   Bunk mattress
25   Reserve torpedoes
26   Torpedo tubes (II and IV, as marked)
27   Hydraulic controls for hydroplane arm drive motor
28   Hydroplane drive motor
29   Transmission shaft for windlass/capstan motor
30   Windlass/capstan motor
31   Attitude control arm for forward hydroplanes
32   Anchor chain locker (free-flooding)

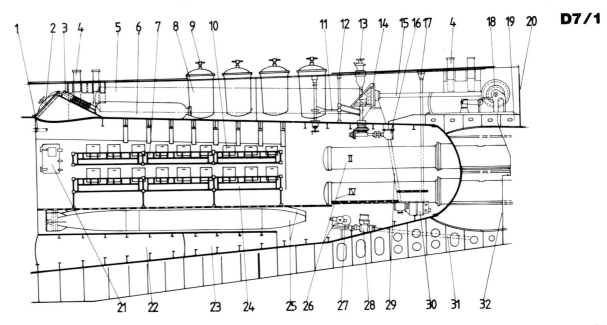

D Compartments

D7/2 **BOW TORPEDO ROOM AND CREW'S QUARTERS, PLAN OF DECK BELOW CASING ABOVE COMPARTMENT**

1 Rear bulkhead of compartment (within pressure hull)
2 Head of Schnorchel (when fitted)
3 Port saddle-tank
4 Line of pressure hull
5 Removable bollards
6 Four 5 man inflatable life raft containers (watertight)
7 Gears for windlass/capstan
8 Control arm for forward diving tank vent
9 Drive shaft for anchor windlass
10 Access and charging plate for high pressure air bottles of group 6
11 Vent for forward diving tank
12 Forward torpedo loading hatch
13 Collision cowling for loading hatch
14 Easing spring for loading hatch
15 High pressure air bottle (part of group 6)
16 Air hoses to forward diving tank and (aft) forward trim tank
17 Reserve torpedo container (watertight)
18 Access plate to air connections to forward diving tank
19 Line of pressure casing bow cap

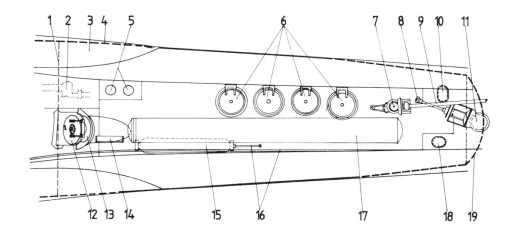

D7/3 **BOW TORPEDO ROOM AND CREW'S QUARTERS, PLAN AT DECK LEVEL**

1 Bulkhead
2 Pressure hull
3 High pressure air bottles of group 4
4 Folding mess table
5 Grating
6 High pressure air bottle for port torpedo tube IV
7 Torpedo tube IV
8 Bunks

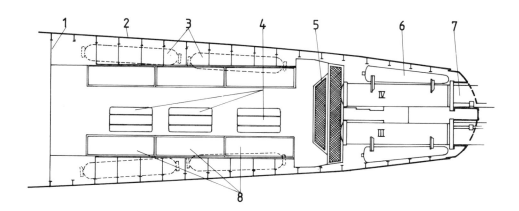

D7/4   **BOW TORPEDO ROOM AND CREW'S QUARTERS, PLAN AT LEVEL OF THE HOLD**
1   Lower bulkhead
2   Hold
3   Frames
4   Bulkhead of torpedo compensating tanks 2 and 3
5   Main water inlet
6   Pressure hull
7   Reserve torpedoes
8   Forward hydroplane motor hydraulic reservoir
9   Forward hydroplane control arm gland

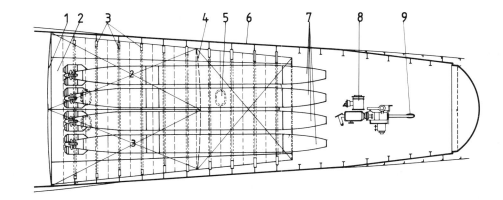

D7/5   **FORWARD TORPEDO ROOM** (general view; no scale)
1   Support beam for torpedo stowage and loading
2   Air blower
3   Light
4   Control wheel for capstan/windlass control
5   Storage space
6   Spares container
7   Torpedo setting dials (repeated from bridge computer)
8   Deck
9   Torpedo tube III
10   Bunk/seat

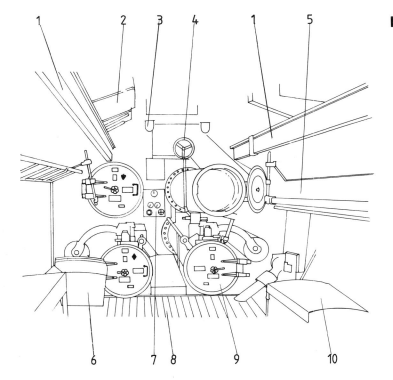

D Compartments

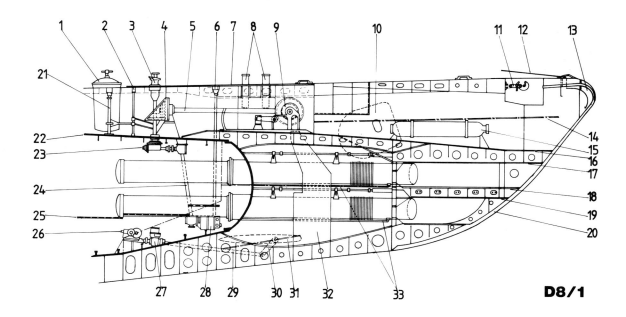

D8/1   **BOW SECTION, INTERNAL PROFILE**

1. Watertight 5 man inflatable life raft container
2. Deck control point for capstan/windlass
3. Capstan head (removable at sea)
4. Mounting for anchor windlass drive shaft
5. Anchor windlass drive shaft
6. Speed/direction control for capstan/windlass motor
7. Outer casing deck
8. Bollards (removable at sea)
9. Anchor windlass
10. Anchor housing (starboard only), with hawse hole shown in solid line
11. Forward towing hook
12. Jumping wire, supporting forward aerial
13. Bow casing reinforcement
14. Stringer II
15. High pressure air bottle
16. 'E' Deck
17. 'D' Deck
18. 'C' Deck (below is stringer III)
19. 'B' Deck
20. Bow casing (bow shown here is the modified Atlantic bow)
21. Selector lever for capstan/windlass control
22. Pressure hull
23. Gear box
24. Motor drive shaft
25. Working deck
26. Hydroplane attitude control motor (hydraulic)
27. Rear housing for hydroplane control arm
28. Capstan/windlass motor (electric)
29. Outline of starboard hydroplane
30. Hydroplane control link arm
31. Stringer I
32. Chain locker
33. Torpedo tube drainage pipes (Stringer III runs alongside the pipe to tube I)

D8/2   **BOW SECTION, ANCHOR, CAPSTAN AND WINDLASS CONTROLS (no scale)**

1. Deck gear control for capstan
2. Deck brake for capstan
3. Selector arm for capstan/windlass drive
4. Capstan (removable at sea)
5. Deck gear control for windlass drive
6. Deck brake for windlass drive
7. Drive shaft for windlass drum
8. Pressure hull fore end
9. Windlass drum
10. Anchor chain
11. Anchor (standard U-boat pattern)
12. Anchor housing (outer casing)
13. Outer casing deck
14. Internal brake for capstan
15. Internal gear control for capstan
16. Drive motor for capstan/windlass
17. Reduction gear box
18. Internal gear control for capstan/windlass drive
19. Internal brake for capstan/windlass drive
20. Diving tank 5
21. Torpedo/crew compartment
22. Chain locker (free-flooding)
23. Line of outer casing below bow

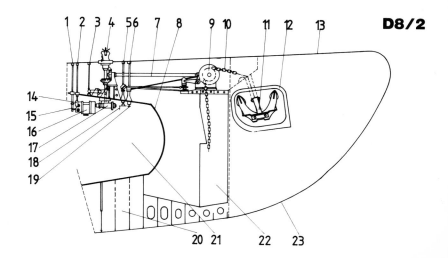

D8/3   **BOW SECTION, PLAN BENEATH CASING LEVEL**
1   Watertight 5 man inflatable life raft container lid
2   Reserve torpedo stowage container (watertight)
3   Gearing for drive to capstan/windlass
4   Blowing vent, forward diving tank
5   Anchor windlass
6   Anchor chain

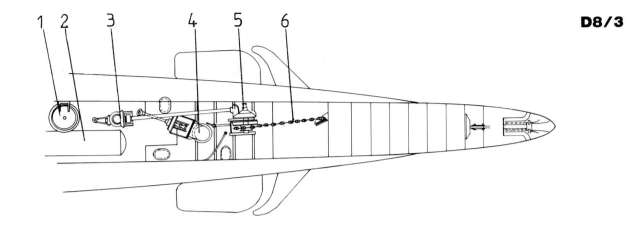

D8/4   **BOW SECTION PLAN AT 'E' DECK (the drawing shows the anchor windlass mountings, anchor hawse hole and the lower central bow support beam)**

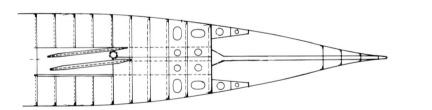

D8/5   **BOW SECTION, PLAN AT 'D' DECK (the drawing shows the upper positions of the torpedo tube door mounting pins as well as the decking at the same level)**

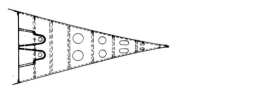

D Compartments

D8/6 **BOW SECTION, PLAN AT 'C' DECK** (the plan shows torpedo tubes III and IV, diving tank 5 and the perforated deck plating which was used throughout to combine required strength with a degree of lightness)

D8/7 **BOW SECTION, STRINGER III** (this stringer was one of the main longitudinal bow supports, and was fitted immediately below 'C' Deck)

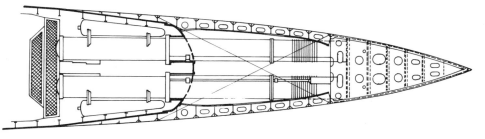

D8/6

D8/7

D8/8 **BOW SECTION, PLAN AT 'B' DECK**
1 Torpedo tube I
2 Torpedo tube mounting plate and collision bulkhead
3 Torpedo tube door mounting pin for tube I
4 Lightening holes in 'B' deck plating

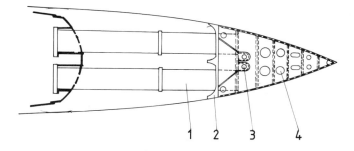

D8/8

1 2 3 4

D8/9 BOW SECTION, PLAN AT 'A' DECK AND STRINGER I

1 External collision bulkhead
2 Hydroplane mounting arm
3 Hydroplane motor hydraulic reservoir
4 Hydroplane motor control linkage from control room (hydraulic)
5 Hydroplane attitude control motor
6 Pressure hull
7 Hydroplane fairing support wire
8 Hydroplane control arm gland in pressure hull
9 Frame 97
10 Hydroplane mounting arm housing
11 Casing gland for hydroplane mounting arm
12 Hydroplane fairing
13 Outer casing
14 Bow collision bulkhead
15 Lightening holes in deck plating
16 Bow reinforcement

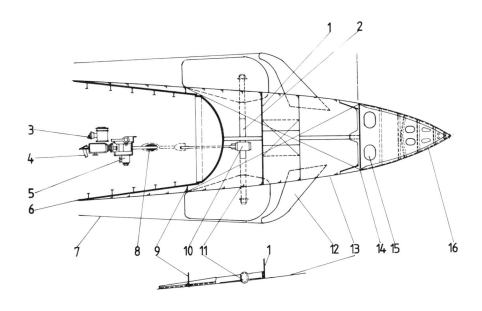

D8/10 UNDERWATER SENSORS (this drawing is a composite, showing the various types of listening equipment available to the Type VII U-boats – most were fitted with one or more of the devices drawn, but none had all of the sets shown)

1 Upper casing drainage slots
2 KDB (*Kristalldrehbasisgerät*) rotating hydrophone (could give bearings to an accuracy of plus or minus 1°, but range was far less than GHG below)
3 Anchor housing
4 Forward casing drainage holes
5 Forward watertight casing (outlined)
6 Forward torpedo room and crew's quarters
7 Outline of pressure hull
8 Drainage slots for lower forward casing
9 Forward hydroplane
10 UT (underwater listening equipment)
11 GHG (*Gruppenhorchgerät* or group listening device) could detect single ships at up to 20km and convoys at nearly 100km. There were originally 11 and then 24 receivers per side
12 Fairing for forward hydroplane
13 Another UT
14 Diving tank 5
15 Bow doors for torpedo tubes numbers I and III
16 Atlantic bow–the original Type VII form is shown as hatched lines

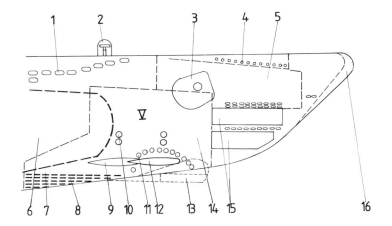

E Armament and fittings

E1   **2cm MG C30 ON WATERTIGHT CANISTER MOUNTING (1/25 scale)**

E1/1   **Elevation**

E1/2   **Plan**
1. Flash guard
2. Mount position when raised for anit-aircraft work
3. Surface action fore sight
4. Cocking handle
5. Ring sight, anti-aircraft targets
6. Rear sight post for surface work
7. Breech cover
8. Gunner's shoulder pads
9. Rotating arm (free-swinging)
10. Fixed sleeve for rotating arm
11. Elevating wheel for mounting (to raise or lower gun)
12. Watertight canister for equipment
13. Safety chain for canister lid
14. Canister lid
15. Deck mounting
16. Barrel
17. 20-round magazine
18. Empty case receiver
19. Firing trigger
20. Gunner's hand grip

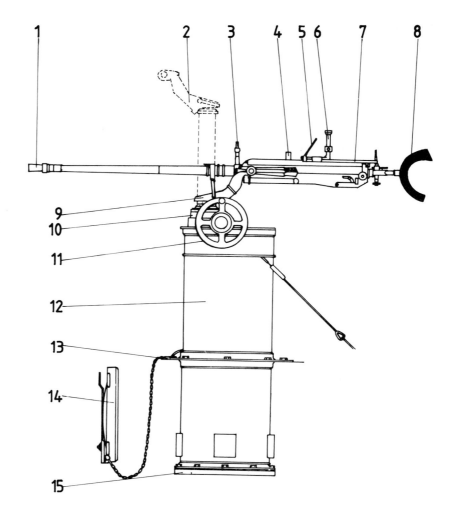

E1/1

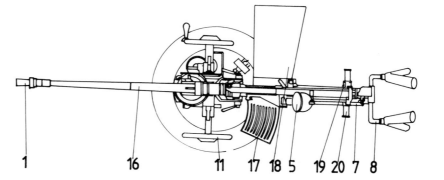

E1/2

E2 **2cm MG C30 ON LC 30/37 MOUNTING**

E2/1 Elevation

E2/2 Plan

E2/3 General view (no scale)

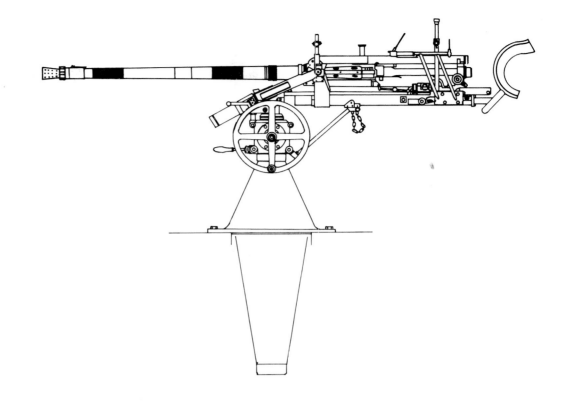

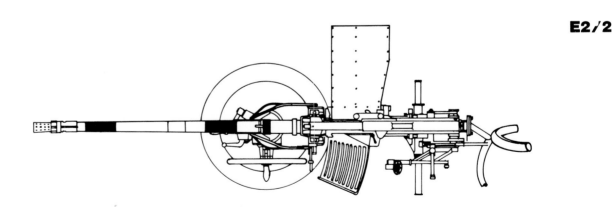

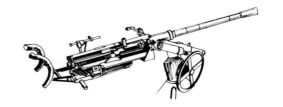

E Armament and fittings

E3

2cm FlaK 38 (1/25 scale)
This weapon was a refinement of
the MG C30, but was initially on the
same mounting as that weapon.

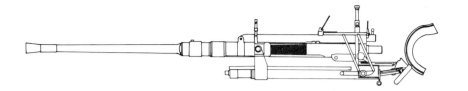

E4

**3.7cm SKC30U ON LC 39
MANUAL LOADING MOUNTING
(1/50 scale)**

E4/1   Elevation

E4/2   **Plan**
1   Gun barrel
2   Travelling lock
3   Recuperator cylinder
4   Gun body
5   Breech housing
6   Ready-to-fire indicator
7   Shield for elevation number
8   Elevation number shoulder piece
     mounting bar
9   Left shoulder piece for elevation
     number
10   Elevation control wheel
11   Fuse setter
12   Gun cradle
13   Traverse control handle
14   Traverse number seat
15   Pedestal
16   Gun mounting base
17   Elevation optical sight
18   Breech block
19   Breech operating lever
20   Traverse sight
21   Lead indicator
22   Mounting bar and transmission
     shaft for traverse controls
23   Barrel slide
24   Stabilising buffer
25   Mounting piston
26   Traverse gearing
27   Gun mount
28   Traverse lock
29   Mounting piston
30   Breech automatic opening linkage
     (on recoil)

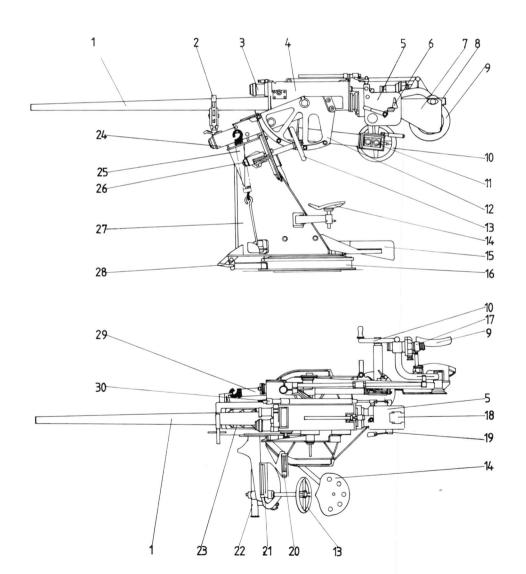

E5   **8.8cm SKC35 ON LC 35 MOUNTING**

E5/1   Elevation (1/50 scale)

E5/2   Plan view (1/50 scale)

E5/3   Front view (1/50 scale)
1   Gun barrel
2   Lead sight
3   Combined elevation and traverse sight (could be mounted either to left or right of gun). Two gunners operated this sight and the firing controls
4   Deflection setting dial for lead sight
5   Pintle
6   Deflection setting handle for lead sight
7   Breech housing
8   Elevator's safety harness
9   Traversing control wheel
10   Elevation control wheel
11   Rear barrel section
12   Recoil tray
13   Mounting counterweight
14   Main mounting body
15   Controls and gearing arm
16   Traverse number's safety harness

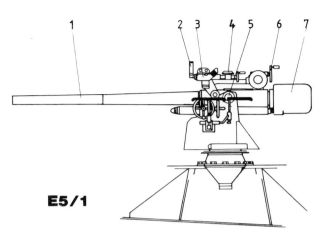

E5/1

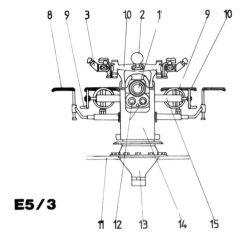

E5/3

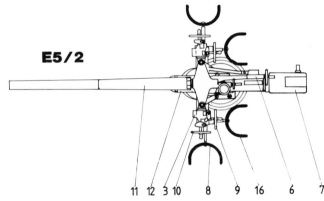
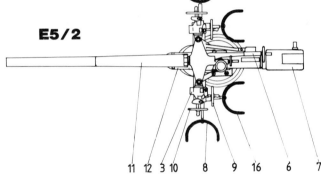

E5/2

E5/4   General view (no scale)

E5/5   Gunsight detail (no scale)

E5/4

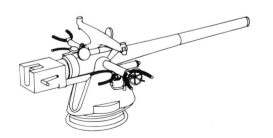

E5/5

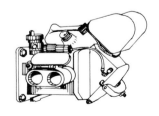

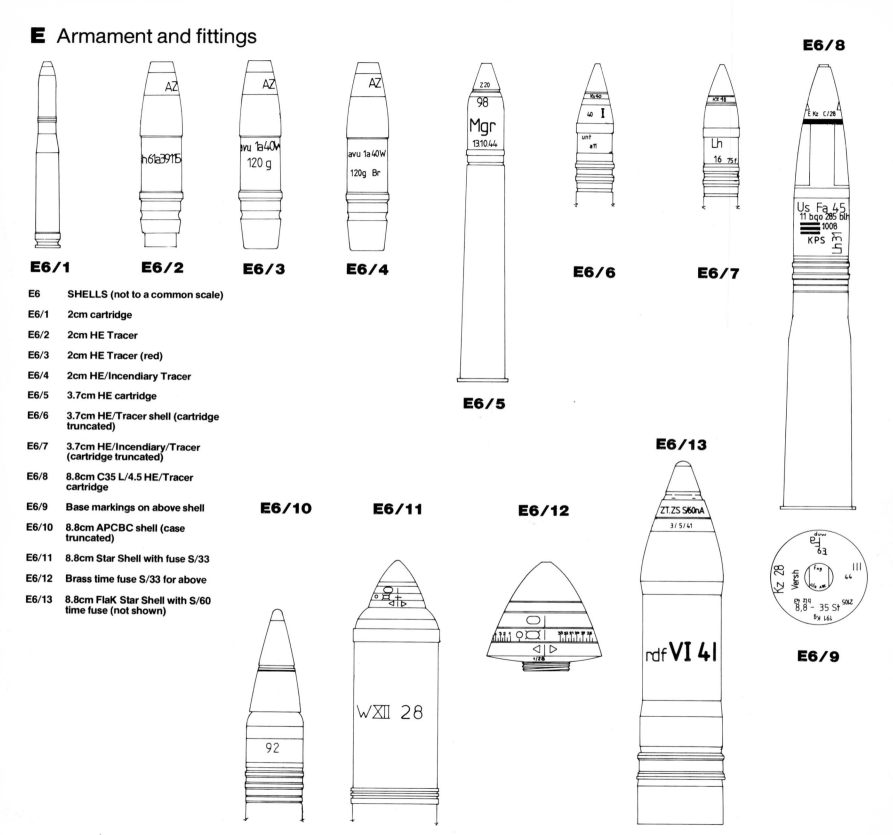

E Armament and fittings

E6/1 **E6/2** **E6/3** **E6/4** **E6/5** **E6/6** **E6/7** **E6/8**

E6   SHELLS (not to a common scale)

E6/1   2cm cartridge

E6/2   2cm HE Tracer

E6/3   2cm HE Tracer (red)

E6/4   2cm HE/Incendiary Tracer

E6/5   3.7cm HE cartridge

E6/6   3.7cm HE/Tracer shell (cartridge truncated)

E6/7   3.7cm HE/Incendiary/Tracer (cartridge truncated)

E6/8   8.8cm C35 L/4.5 HE/Tracer cartridge

E6/9   Base markings on above shell

E6/10   8.8cm APCBC shell (case truncated)

E6/11   8.8cm Star Shell with fuse S/33

E6/12   Brass time fuse S/33 for above

E6/13   8.8cm FlaK Star Shell with S/60 time fuse (not shown)

E6/10 **E6/11** **E6/12** **E6/13** **E6/9**

E7 TORPEDOES

E7/1 53.3cm G7e TORPEDO (1/30 scale)

1	Firing pistol (here the G7H is shown)	6	Rear body and electric motor housing
2	Practice warhead	7	Depth keeping fins (both sides)
3	Warhead	8	Attitude fins
4	Main body and battery container	9	Attitude adjusters (controlled by internal gyro-compass)
5	Green torpedo-type markings (positions varied)	10	Contra-rotating propellers

E7/1

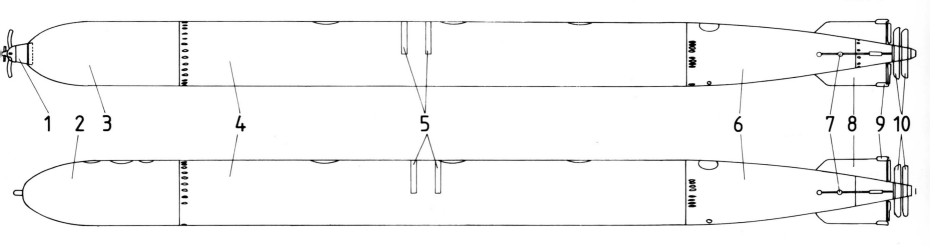

1 2 3   4   5   6   7 8 9 10

E7/2 G7a TORPEDOES (1/30 scale)

This is the first service torpedo used by the U-boat Arm in the Second World War and was propelled by compressed air. The emission of a stream of bubbles from the outlet at the tail made the torpedo too obvious in daylight, and it was soon superseded by the G7e. The lower view shows the practice head.

E7/2

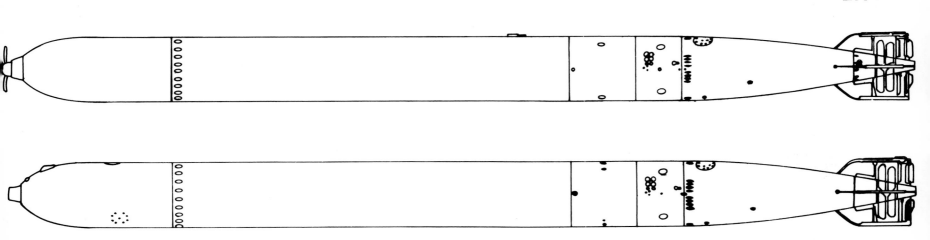

E Armament and fittings

E8 TORPEDO TUBE II (PORT SIDE, UPPER)

E8/1 Starboard elevation (no scale)

E8/2 Plan view (no scale)
1. Tube cap handle
2. Tube cap
3. Manual firing lever
4. Firing arm
5. Firing pin
6. Electromagnetic firing coil
7. Cocking arm
8. Air ventilator
9. Arm support
10. Gyro setting arm
11. Torpedo inspection port dock
12. Torpedo inspection port release catch
13. High pressure air bottle (for venting tube on reloading)
14. Bow door hinge
15. Bow door
16. Compensating tank (schematic)
17. Inlet/outlet valve for tube
18. Water line (schematic)
19. Bow cap of pressure hull
20. Bow casing tube support bulkhead
21. Tube stabilising plate
22. Manual control for bow door
23. Safety plate
24. Bow door control linkage
25. Bow door/firing mechanism safety
26. Gyro setting arm fine adjustment screw
27. Gyro manual adjustment
28. Depth setting dial

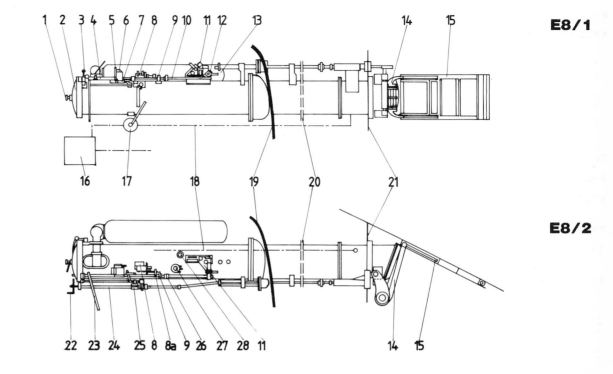

E8/1

E8/2

E9 TORPEDO LOADING GEAR (no scale)
1. Rear hitch
2. Tensioning wire
3. Sheerleg post
4. Torpedo safety wire
5. Torpedo being loaded
6. Torpedo cradle
7. Nose guide
8. Forward torpedo loading hatch door
9. Loading wire
10. Winch head
11. Winch gearbox
12. Torpedo in loading position for reload
13. Torpedo in second loading position before stowing
14. Hand ratchet
15. Stowage platform
16. Carrying cradle
17. Outer casing
18. Pressure hull
19. Torpedo tubes
20. Torpedo nose cup
21. Buffer

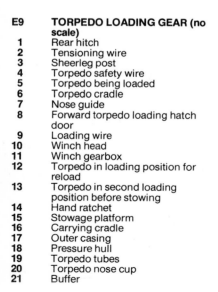
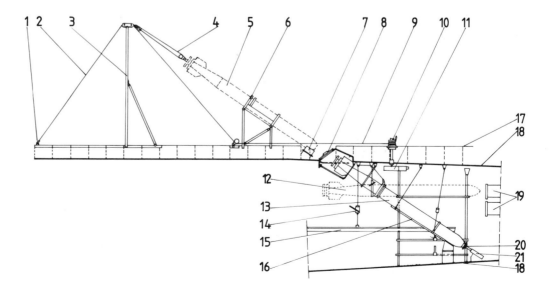

E9

E10 BRIDGE FITTINGS (no scale)

E10/1 CONTROL ROOM PERISCOPE

1. Periscope pressure hull housing
2. Water bleeder
3. Head angle setting wheel (–15° to +50°)
4. Illumination control box
5. Illumination control wheel
6. Magnification control arm
7. Eyepiece
8. Arm/hand rest and rotation control
9. Base link
10. Retraction cable

E10/2 EARLY TYPE SCHNORCHEL

E10/3 LATER TYPE SCHNORCHEL HEAD

E10/4 FuMB 7, 'NAXOS' AERIAL

E10/5 FuMB AERIAL 2, 'METOX' ('BISCAY CROSS')

E10/6 UZO (Unterseeboots Ziel Ortungsgerät – submarine target binoculars and transmitter; no scale)

1. Rough alignment sight
2. Binoculars
3. UZO transmitting head (giving bearing to target and lay-off angle)
4. Traversing arm
5. Locking nut
6. Angular scale (0° was head of the boat)

E10/1

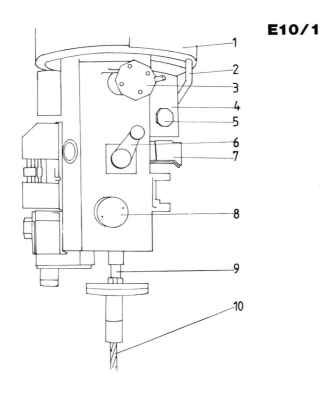

E10/2

E10/3

E10/4

E10/5

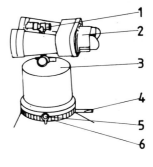

E10/6